P: As   #5

1 # 35

Elongation
Elasticity
Shear & Bending Moment
Select A Beam
Centroid & Moments of Inertia
composite Steel Plate on Top & Bottom

Essential Strength of Materials

Essential
Strength of Materials

FREDERICK R. LISARELLI

Purdue University

McGRAW-HILL BOOK COMPANY, INC.

New York   Toronto   London   1957

ESSENTIAL STRENGTH OF MATERIALS

Library of Congress Catalog Card Number: 57-8011

THE MAPLE PRESS COMPANY, YORK, PA.

PREFACE

This book was written for use in courses in strength of materials which emphasize the applied and practical rather than the abstract and theoretical. It is designed for programs in which the student has not completed a course in calculus as preparation for courses in applied mathematics. As such it is hoped that the book will be useful in courses in technical institutes, community colleges, extension programs, and technical training in industry.

The theory of strength of materials has been developed with the use of algebra and trigonometry alone. Formulas which cannot be derived without the use of calculus have been assumed. Examples are worked out in detail without leaving any steps to be supplied by the student. The problems are direct applications of the principles which immediately precede them. Tables of properties of materials are included as they become necessary for the solution of problems.

A section on accuracy of computation and significant figures has been included to permit the student to "round off" his answers according to principle rather than to his imagination.

A physical explanation of the modulus of elasticity has been included for better understanding of the relation of unit stress to unit strain.

The section on riveted joints contains a comparison of the codes of the three most important agencies governing the design and fabrication of riveted joints and a detailed procedure for their design. The section on welded joints has been developed in accordance with the American Welding Society recommendations and includes the calculation of the strength of welded joints and a comparison of the relative strength of welded and riveted joints.

The use of the shear-area method for the construction of bending-moment diagrams has been included to permit the use of the moment-area method for the derivation of deflection formulas.

A chapter on centroids and moment of inertia has been included primarily for the student who desires a course in strength without one in statics. It can also be used advantageously as a review in preparation for beam design. Torsion is studied after beam design to allow the use of the flexure formula in the derivation of the torque formula.

The author wishes to acknowledge his indebtedness to the late Ralph E. Waterhouse for his constant encouragement and assistance in the preparation of the material. He also wishes to thank Nancy Cheney and Marlene Duff for the typing of the manuscript.

FREDERICK R. LISARELLI

CONTENTS

10: Torsion   219

Torsional Loads and Twisting Moment or Torque   The Torque Formula   The Torque Formula for Solid Circular Shafts   The Torque Formula for Hollow Shafts   Angle of Twist of a Cylindrical Shaft   Torque, Horsepower, and RPM   Flexure and Torsion Combined   Procedure for Designing Shafts

Helical Springs

1: Simple Stresses

1-1. Introduction

Strength of materials is that branch of mechanics which treats of the forces acting upon elastic bodies and the resulting changes in form and dimensions.

The external forces that act on the body are called *loads;* the internal forces which resist the external loads are called stresses; the resulting changes in form and dimensions of the body are called *deformations* or *strains*.

External forces which tend to elongate, compress, or shear a body are called *simple direct forces*, as tensile force, compressive force, and shearing force. The internal resistances which tend to keep the body from being pulled apart, from being crushed or shortened, or from being cut in two are called *tensile* stress, *compressive* stress, and *shearing* stress. Figure 1-1 shows examples of tension, compression, and shear.

Tension. Two forces which are equal in magnitude and pull opposite each other in direction along the same line of action will tend to elongate a body, thereby causing tension in the body. The cable supporting an elevator or a bridge has to resist a pull applied at each end.

Compression. Two forces which are equal in magnitude and push toward each other in direction along the same line of action will tend to shorten a body, thereby causing compression. The columns between two floors of a building have to resist a push at each end.

Shear. Two forces which are equal in magnitude and pull opposite each other along parallel lines of action will cause relative sliding or slipping of adjacent portions of the body in parallel lines. This condition is called *shear*. Rivets and other types of fasteners in structural members are examples of bodies under a shearing stress.

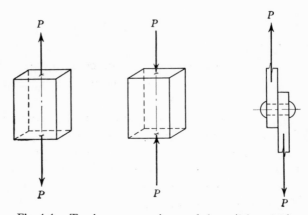

Fig. 1-1.   Tension, compression, and shear (*left to right*).

Tensile and compressive stresses are caused by forces perpendicular to the areas resisting these forces, whereas shearing stresses are caused by forces acting along the resisting area or parallel to it. For this reason, tensile and compressive stresses may be called *normal* stresses, and shearing stresses, *tangential* stresses.

There are two general types of problems involved:

1. To determine whether the elements of machines or structures are capable of withstanding known external loads without failure due to excessive deformation or to the development of excessive internal stresses.

2. To determine the size and shape of the element which will withstand successfully the known external loads without developing excessive deformations or excessive internal stresses.

The solution of these problems depends on a mathematical analysis of the forces acting on the element. This is usually determined by applying the principles of statics. It also depends on certain physical properties, experimentally determined, which vary with the different types of materials used and the manner in which the loads are applied.

Either stress or deformation may be the governing factor in both of these general problems. Usually, the type of work to be performed by the given machine or structure determines whether stress or deformation is the limiting criterion. In the main, internal stress is the factor which governs the design of most machines and structures. If the stress developed does not exceed a certain limiting value, the design is considered satisfactory from a standpoint of strength.

However, there are certain types of structures such as motors, engines, and other machines which contain moving parts or perform functions in which dimensional changes must be confined to very narrow limits. For these, deformation may well be the governing factor of design.

1-2. Accuracy of Computation. Significant Figures

At this point, it might be well to consider the degree of accuracy of computation required in any given problem or situation.

In general, numbers obtained by measurement are approximate. If the length of a shaft is expressed as $12\frac{1}{8}$ in., it is implied that the length is given to the nearest eighth of an inch, or that the actual length is between $12\frac{1}{16}$ and $12\frac{3}{16}$ in. If the length is expressed as 12.1 in., the actual length may be any value between 12.05 and 12.15 in.; if expressed as 12.12 in., between 12.115 and 12.125 in., etc.

The significant figures of a number are all the digits of a number which may be present, reading from left to right, including zero when it is not used merely to fix the decimal point. It should be noted that the number of significant figures does not depend on the location of the decimal point. Thus, the numbers 1.25, 0.00125, and 125 each have three significant figures, while 102.5 and 125.0 each have four significant figures. The zeros in the latter two numbers were not used merely to fix the decimal place.

There is one exception to the rule for determining the number of significant figures. If the zeros occur at the end of a whole number, such as 125,000, they may or may not be significant. For instance, if it is stated that the ultimate strength of a certain steel is 65,000 psi (pounds per square inch), it is not to be implied that this value is correct to the nearest pound per square inch, but that it is closer to 65,000 psi than to 64,000 or 66,000 psi. The zeros simply locate the decimal place and are not significant. However, if it is stated that there are 360 degrees in a circle, the value is correct to three significant figures, since the zero in this case does not merely locate the decimal point. Whether the zeros of the end of a whole number are significant or not must be determined by the data supplied.

A form which is frequently used in scientific notation to indicate the accuracy of a number is to write it as the product of two factors. The first factor contains the significant figures of the number; the second, the power of 10 required to fix the decimal place. For example, if we wish to indicate that the ultimate strength of 65,000 psi is correct to two significant figures, we write it 65×10^3 psi. If it actually were correct to five significant figures, we then would write it 65.000×10^3 psi.

In performing arithmetic computations, results can be no more accurate than the least accurate of the given numbers.

The following two rules are frequently used in determining the accuracy of results:

1. In the sum (or difference) of two or more numbers, a place is significant only if it is significant in every number used in the operation.

2. In the product (or quotient) of two or more numbers, the result should contain only as many significant figures as are found in that original number with the least significant figures.

Thus, if we multiply 65,000 psi by 0.0625 sq in., we should obtain 4,100 lb.

1-3. Stresses Due to Central Loads

A concentrated load whose line of action passes through the centroid of an area is called a *central* load. A distributed load whose resultant passes through the centroid may also be considered as a central load. The internal stress produced on a straight bar of constant cross section by a central load may be assumed to be uniformly distributed over the cross-sectional area. Since *unit stress* is defined to be internal stress per unit of area, it will therefore be constant under a central load.

If we know how much load a square inch or square foot of surface can sustain, we may determine the total load the surface can sustain by multiplying the total area by the load per unit of area.

Thus, if P = total external load, lb

A = cross sectional area, sq in.

s = unit stress, psi

then $$P = As \qquad (1\text{-}1)$$

This equation is considered as valid for all three principal types of stresses: tensile, compressive, and shear. Actually, shearing stress is practically never uniformly distributed.

Therefore, the unit shearing stress used in this equation must be the *average* shearing stress.

Example 1-1.   Determine the tensile load which a steel bar 4 in. diam will support if the unit stress is 15,000 psi.

SOLUTION: Given

$$s = 15,000 \text{ psi}$$
$$A = \pi r^2 = (3.1416)(2)^2 = 12.57 \text{ sq in.}$$

Substituting,

$$P = As$$
$$P = (12.57)(15,000) = 189,000 \text{ lb} \qquad \text{ANS.}$$

Example 1-2.   A 4- by 4-in. column supports a load of 12,000 lb. Find the unit stress developed in the column.

SOLUTION: Given

$$P = 12,000 \text{ lb}$$
$$A = (4)(4) = 16 \text{ sq in.}$$
$$s = ?$$

Substituting,

$$P = As$$
$$12,000 = 16s$$
$$s = 750 \text{ psi} \qquad \text{ANS.}$$

PROBLEMS

1-1.   A structural steel rod 2 in. diam supports a load of 100,000 lb. Find the unit stress.

1-2.   A platform is supported by four short cast-iron legs 5 in. diam, one at each corner.   Determine the total allowable load if the unit working stress must not exceed 15,000 psi.

1-3.   What load is necessary to stress a $\frac{1}{2}$-in.-diam test bar to 30,000 psi?

1-4.   Determine the unit stress developed in a 6- by 6-in. wooden block if it carries a compressive load of 32,000 lb.

1-5.   Determine the diameter of a wrought-iron bar which is to support a load of 200,000 lb if the allowable unit stress is 12,500 psi.

4 $\frac{1}{2}$

1-6. In Prob. 1-5, if the bar is 1¾ in. thick, what should be its width?

1-7. A short cast-iron post with a 10 in. OD and 8 in. ID carries a compressive load of 45,000 lb. Determine the unit stress developed.

1-8. Commercial steel bars vary in thickness by sixteenths of an inch. Determine the commercial size of a steel bar which will support a load of 72,000 lb if the unit stress must not exceed 18,000 psi and the width of the bar is 5 in. $\frac{13}{16}$

1-9. A platform 20 by 45 ft is to support a uniformly distributed load of 20 psi. It rests on fifty 6- by 6-in. timber posts. What is the unit stress developed in each post?

1-10. A 12- by 12- by 8-ft bin is filled to the top with sand. If sand weighs 100 lb per cu ft, what size timber posts will be required at each corner, if the allowable working stress must not exceed 1,000 psi. *10,¾   9,5*

1-4. Stresses at Oblique Sections of Axially Loaded Members

In a body subject to axially applied tensile or compressive loads, stresses will be induced not only on planes perpendicular to the direction of the load, but also on every diagonal plane in that body. In the former case, $P = As$ applies.

Figure 1-2*a* shows a body under the action of axial tensile loads at each end. It is desired to determine the magnitude of the stresses normal and tangential to any oblique plane making an angle θ (theta) with a cross section perpendicular to the applied load.

Figure 1-2*b* is a free-body diagram with the lower force P resolved into its components normal (P_n) and tangential (P_t) to the oblique plane, but

$$P_n = P \cos \theta$$
and
$$P_t = P \sin \theta$$

The area on which these component forces act is

$$A' = bc = \frac{ba}{\cos \theta} = \frac{A}{\cos \theta}$$

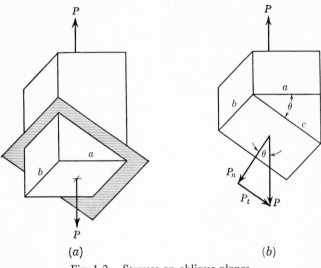

(a)   (b)

Fig. 1-2.   Stresses on oblique planes.

where $A = ab$, the area of the cross section.   Dividing the component forces by this area gives shearing unit stress:

$$s_s = \frac{P \sin \theta}{A/\cos \theta} = \frac{P}{A} \sin \theta \cos \theta = \frac{P}{A} \frac{\sin 2\theta}{2} = \frac{P}{2A} \sin 2\theta \quad (1\text{-}2)$$

and normal unit stress:

$$s_n = \frac{P \cos \theta}{A/\cos \theta} = \frac{P}{A} \cos^2 \theta = \frac{P}{A} \left(\frac{1}{2} + \frac{1}{2} \cos 2\theta \right)$$
$$= \frac{P}{2A} + \frac{P}{2A} \cos 2\theta \quad (1\text{-}3)$$

Mohr's circle is an ingenious device which allows a visual interpretation of these two formulas for normal and shearing stresses on diagonal planes.

On rectangular S_n-S_s axes, draw a circle with center O on the S_n axis, with a radius equal to $P/2A$ and tangent to the S_s axis (Fig. 1-3).   Turn off angle 2θ counterclockwise at the center of circle O, the turning radius $(P/2A)$ intersecting the circumference of the circle at Q.

Angle θ is the angle between the plane perpendicular to the applied load and the plane under consideration. As point Q travels about the circle, the value of its abscissa

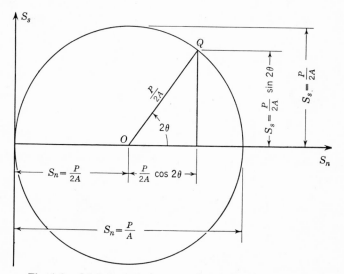

Fig. 1-3.   Mohr's circle for normal and shearing stresses.

equals the normal unit stress, and of its ordinate, the shearing unit stress for the particular value of 2θ used.

We note that when $\theta = 0°$, the normal stress from Eq. (1-3) becomes

$$s_n = \frac{P}{2A} + \frac{P(1)}{2A}$$

$$s_n = \frac{P}{A}$$

which verifies the statements of Art. 1-3.   This also reveals that only in a plane perpendicular to the axis of the applied load is the *maximum normal stress* obtained.

10 Simple Stresses

Also, when $\theta = 0°$, there is no shearing stress, since, from Eq. (1-2),

$$s_s = \frac{P(0)}{2A}$$

$$s_s = 0$$

Thus, when $\theta = 0°$, or, on every plane perpendicular to the axis of the applied load, the normal stress is a maximum, and the shearing stress is a minimum (zero).

The shearing stress will be a maximum when $\theta = 45°$, since

$$s_s = \frac{P}{2A} \sin 2\theta = \frac{P}{2A} \sin 90° = \frac{P(1)}{2A}$$

$$s_s = \frac{P}{2A}$$

Note that the maximum shearing unit stress equals only one-half of the maximum normal unit stress.

It is important to determine oblique stresses whenever materials are involved whose rupture strength in shear is less than one-half the corresponding tensile or compressive strength, since the shearing unit stress would reach its limiting value first.

Example 1-3. A steel bar 2 in. square carries an axially applied load of 50,000 lb. Compute (*a*) the unit stress on the bar and (*b*) the normal and shearing stresses on planes making 30° and 45°, respectively, with the cross section.

SOLUTION:

(*a*) $$s = \frac{P}{A} = \frac{50,000}{2 \times 2} = 12,500 \text{ psi}$$

(*b*) For a plane at 30° with the cross section

$$s_n = \frac{P}{2A} + \frac{P}{2A} \cos 2\theta$$

$$s_n = \frac{50,000}{2 \times 4} + \frac{50,000}{2 \times 4}\frac{1}{2} = 6,250 + 3,125 = 9,375 \text{ psi}$$

$$s_S = \frac{P}{2A} \sin 2\theta$$

$$= \frac{50,000}{2 \times 4}\frac{\sqrt{3}}{2} = 5,400 \text{ psi}$$

(c) For a plane at 45° with the cross section

$$s_n = \frac{50,000}{2 \times 4} + \frac{50,000}{2 \times 4}(\cos 90°) = 6,250 \text{ psi}$$

$$s_S = \frac{50,000}{2 \times 4}(\sin 90°) = 6,250 \text{ psi}$$

PROBLEMS

odds 11-25

1-11. A short bar ¾ in. square carries a tensile load of 18,000 lb. Compute the unit stress on the bar, and also the normal and shear stresses on a plane making 45° with the cross section.

1-12. Work Prob. 1-11 graphically by using Mohr's circle.

1-13. In Prob. 1-11, what are the normal and shearing unit stresses acting on a plane making 30° with the cross section?

1-14. A test specimen 1 in. diam and 2 in. long failed on a plane making an angle of 45° with its cross section when subjected to a load of 75,000 lb. Find the normal and shearing unit stresses acting on the plane at the time of failure.

1-15. If the allowable stresses in compression and shear for cast iron are 15,000 and 3,000 psi, what is the safe load for a short post 2 in. diam?

1-16. What maximum compressive load may be applied to a 4- × 4-in. timber post if the grain of the wood makes an angle of 45° with the length of the post? The allowable stresses are 1,000 and 150 psi in compression and shear, respectively.

1-5. Working Stress. Allowable Working Stress

Working stresses are the unit stresses to which the members of a machine or structure are subjected. The allowable working stress for any given material is the maximum unit stress which should be applied to this material according to the judgment of some competent and official authority.

Table 1-1 gives the allowable stresses in tension, compression, and shear for some of the more common materials.

These numbers are only average values for use in the solution of problems. They are based on the assumption that the structure carries a dead load, such as machines fixed in place. In the case of a live load that may produce varying stresses which may even change from tension to compression or shear, the allowable working stress will be much lower.

Table 1-1. *Allowable Working Stresses, psi*

MATERIAL	TENSION	COMPRESSION	SHEAR
Structural steel	20,000	20,000	12,000
Cast steel	16,000	16,000	9,000
Wrought iron	12,000	12,000	8,000
Cast iron	3,000	15,000	3,000
Duralumin	15,000	15,000	10,000
Brass (70–30)	12,000	12,000	8,000
Bronze	10,000	10,000	7,000
Timber, average:			
With grain	. . . . . .	1,000	150
Across grain	. . . . . .	300	

PROBLEMS

1-17. Calculate the total compressive load which may be applied to a 6- by 6-in. short timber block, parallel to grain and across grain.

1-18. A structural-steel eyebar 1 in. thick exerts a pull of 60,000 lb. Calculate its minimum width.

1-19. What is the allowable tensile load on a 4¼-in.-diam structural-steel rod 4½ ft long? Shear load?

1-20. Determine the allowable load in compression and shear on a cast-iron rod 3½ in. diam.

1-6. Strain. Unit Strain

The changes in size that occur when stresses are applied to a body are called *deformations* or *strains*. These strains will vary according to the type of external stress applied; a tensile, compressive, or shearing force will produce a corresponding internal tensile, compressive, or shearing stress with the resulting strains.

Unit strain is the strain per unit length of a body. It is found by dividing the total deformation by the length of the body.

Expressed in mathematical form, unit strain is generally represented by the Greek letter ϵ (epsilon). Total strain, or deformation, in a length L is generally expressed by the letter e. In equation form then, unit strain is

$$\epsilon = \frac{e}{L} \tag{1-4}$$

expressed as inches per inch, if both total strain, e, and length, L, are expressed in inches.

This value could have been called *unit elongation* if the applied load had been tensile, causing the member to lengthen, or *unit contraction* if the load had been compressive, causing it to contract.

The value of unit strain, being obtained by dividing a length by a length, is an abstract number or ratio. Thus, a bar 10 in. long which has a total deformation of 0.1 in. has a unit strain imposed upon it of 0.01 in. per in. of length.

1-7. Elastic Limit

When a stress is applied to a body, a corresponding strain is produced. When the stress is removed, the body will return to its original size and shape, provided the unit stress developed by the applied force has not exceeded a certain limit. If the stress has gone beyond this limit, the body will not return to its original size and shape, but will retain a permanent deformation or set. The unit stress at this limit is called the *elastic limit* of the material. Thus, the elastic limit is the maximum unit stress which can be imposed on a body without causing permanent strain. Within the elastic limit, the strain produced is directly proportional to the stress applied. This law is called *Hooke's law*, in honor of Robert Hooke, the English scientist who first demonstrated it in 1678.

Table 1-2 lists the elastic limit under tension and compression for some of the more commonly used materials.

Table 1-2. *Elastic Limit, psi*

MATERIAL	TENSION	COMPRESSION	SHEAR
Structural steel	35,000	35,000	21,000
Wrought iron	30,000	30,000	18,000
Malleable iron	30,000	30,000	20,000
Cast iron	6,000	25,000	
Nickel steel	50,000	50,000	38,000
Timber (with grain)	3,200	3,000	
Stone	. . . . . .	2,000	
Aluminum alloy 17ST	32,000	32,000	21,000
Copper, hard drawn	40,000	40,000	23,000
Brass (70–30)	25,000	25,000	15,000
Bronze	25,000	25,000	15,000

BRONZE

Example 1-4. Determine the diameter of a wrought-iron rod which is to be under a tension of 75,000 lb so that the unit stress will not exceed one-fourth of its elastic limit.

SOLUTION: Given

$$P = 75,000$$
$$s = \tfrac{1}{4}\,(25,000) = 6,250 \text{ psi}$$
$$A = ?$$
$$d = ?$$

Substituting,

$$P = As$$
$$75,000 = 6,250A$$
$$A = 12 \text{ sq in.}$$

Substituting in

$$A = \frac{\pi}{4} d^2$$

$$12 = \frac{3.1416}{4} d^2$$

$$d^2 = 15.28$$
$$d = 3.91 \text{ in.}$$

$e = in$
$E = Psi$
$s = Psi$
$E = in/in$

Commercial size is $3\frac{15}{16}$ in.   ANS.

PROBLEMS

1-21. A timber post 3 in. thick is under a tension of 15,000 lb. Compute its width so that the unit stress may not exceed one-third of its elastic limit.

1-22. Determine the allowable load which can be suspended on a 4-in.-diam structural-steel rod if the unit stress is not to exceed one-fourth of the elastic limit.

1-23. Compute the diameter of a wrought-iron rod which is to be under a compressive load of 75,000 lb in order that the allowable unit stress may not exceed one-fourth of the elastic limit.

1-24. Determine the cross section of a square stick of timber to carry a compressive load of 60,000 lb if the allowable unit stress is not to exceed one-third of the elastic limit.

1-25. An aluminum plate is to hold a load of 25,000 lb in tension. If it is $\frac{3}{4}$ in. thick, what must be its width if the unit stress is not to exceed one-third of the elastic limit?

1-26. What must be the size of a square stone pillar which is to support a compressive load of 50,000 lb?   The unit stress must not exceed one-half of the elastic limit.

1-8. Modulus of Elasticity

Young's modulus or modulus of elasticity is the ratio of the unit stress to the corresponding unit strain, provided the unit stress does not exceed the elastic limit.   It is a measure of a body's stiffness or rigidity, and it is constant within the elastic limit. Modulus of elasticity is represented in mathematical equations by the letter E. Since E is a ratio of the unit stress to unit strain, this relation may be expressed as follows:

$$E = \frac{s}{\epsilon} \qquad (1\text{-}5)$$

where E = modulus of elasticity, psi

s = unit stress, psi

ϵ = unit strain, in. per in.

Since $s = P/A$ and $\epsilon = e/L$, substituting equals for equals,

$$E = \frac{P/A}{e/L} = \frac{P}{A} \times \frac{L}{e}$$

$$E = \frac{PL}{Ae} \qquad (1\text{-}6)$$

Table 1-3 lists the modulus of elasticity under tension and compression for some of the more commonly used materials.

Table 1-3.   *Modulus of Elasticity*

MATERIAL	MODULUS OF ELASTICITY, PSI
Structural steel	30,000,000
Wrought iron	25,000,000
Cast iron	15,000,000
Copper	15,000,000
Brass	14,000,000
Bronze	12,000,000
Aluminum	10,000,000
Timber	1,500,000
Concrete	2,000,000

Example 1-5.   A wrought-iron bar with a cross-sectional area of 2 sq in. and 10 ft long is suspended from one end. Determine the load on the other end that will lengthen it 0.04 in.

SOLUTION: Given

$$A = 2 \text{ sq in.}$$
$$L = 10 \text{ ft} \times 12 = 120 \text{ in.}$$
$$e = 0.04 \text{ in.}$$
$$E = 25,000,000 \text{ psi}$$
$$P = ?$$

Substituting,

$$E = \frac{PL}{Ae}$$

$$25,000,000 = \frac{120P}{2(0.04)}$$

$$P = 16,700 \text{ lb} \quad \text{ANS.}$$

Example 1-6. A steel bar 4 ft long and 1 sq in. in cross section is suspended vertically with a load of 12,000 lb hanging from the bottom end. Compute total elongation and unit elongation.

SOLUTION: Given

$$E = 30,000,000 \text{ psi}$$
$$P = 12,000 \text{ lb.}$$
$$L = 4 \text{ ft} \times 12 = 48 \text{ in.}$$
$$A = 1 \text{ sq in.}$$
$$e = ?$$
$$\epsilon = ?$$

Substituting,

$$E = \frac{PL}{Ae}$$

$$30,000,000 = \frac{(12,000)48}{e}$$

$$e = 0.019 \text{ in. (total elongation)} \quad \text{ANS.}$$

To find unit elongation,

$$\epsilon = \frac{e}{L} = \frac{0.019}{48}$$

$$\epsilon = 0.0004 \text{ in. per in.} \quad \text{ANS.}$$

PROBLEMS

1-27. A $2\frac{1}{4}$-in.-diam steel rod 12 ft long elongates 0.05 in. by suspending a load from its lower end. Compute the load.

1-28. A cast-iron pillar 10 ft diam and 10 ft high supports a load of 10 tons.   Compute total and unit contraction.

1-29. A copper wire 18 ft long and 1/8 in. diam elongates 9/16 in. when a load is suspended from its lower end.   Find the load.

1-30. A 1½-in.-diam steel bar 10 ft long is suspended from one end.   Determine the load at the other end which will elongate it 0.05 in.

1-31. A 2- by 2-in. copper rod contracts 0.0005 in. under a load of 1 ton.   Determine its original length.

1-32. How much will a wrought-iron bar 4 by 4 in. in cross section by 1½ ft long shorten under a load of 100,000 lb?

1-33. A 4-ft long steel bar elongates 0.02 in. under a load of 12,000 lb.   Compute its diameter.

1-34. A 9/16-in.-diam steel test bar 8 in. long stretches 0.00715 in. under a tensile load of 6,400 lb.   Compute the unit stress, unit deformation, and modulus of elasticity.

1-35. A concrete cylinder 8 in. diam and 15 in. long carries a load of 20,000 lb.   Determine total and unit contraction.

1-36. A 2- by 2-in. steel test bar 1 ft 8 in. long is subjected to a tensile load of 140,000 lb.   If it elongates 0.000175 in., what is its modulus of elasticity?

1-9. Physical Meaning of E

The formula $E = s/\epsilon$ may be written in the form $\epsilon = s/E$. If we let s equal unity, then $\epsilon = 1/E$.   Using the common engineering units, this equation states the following: The reciprocal of E is numerically equal to the unit strain or deformation produced by a unit load of one pound per square inch of cross-sectional area.

The modulus of elasticity of steel is approximately 30,000,000 psi.   This means that a pull of 1 lb on a steel bar of 1 sq in. in cross-sectional area will stretch every inch of length of this bar 1/30,000,000 of an inch.   A pull of 1,000 lb per sq in. of cross section will stretch each inch of length 1,000/30,000,000 or 1/30,000 of an inch.   A pull of 30,000 psi will stretch the bar 30,000/30,000,000, or 1/1,000, of an inch per inch of length.

1-10. Ultimate Strength

When any member of a machine structure is subjected to a unit stress in excess of its elastic limit, that member is usually unsafe. As the stress is increased, the deformation in that member increases rapidly. If the stress exceeds a certain limit, the member will fail.

Ultimate strength is that limit, or highest unit stress that a material can bear just prior to its breaking. Ultimate strengths are usually two to four times their elastic limits.

The ultimate strength of a material in tension is called *ultimate tensile strength;* in compression, *ultimate compressive strength;* in shear, *ultimate shearing strength.* Since ultimate strength is a unit stress, it is expressed in pounds per square inch.

Table 1-4 lists the ultimate tensile and compressive strengths of several commonly used materials.

Table 1-4.   *Ultimate Strength, psi*

MATERIAL	TENSION	COMPRESSION
Structural steel	65,000	60,000
Wrought iron	50,000	50,000
Cast iron	20,000	90,000
Malleable cast iron	30,000	46,000
Timber (with grain)	10,000	8,000

Example 1-7.   Find the ultimate tensile strength of a ½-in. square steel test bar which failed at a pull of 14,200 lb.

SOLUTION: Given

$$P = 14,200 \text{ lb}$$
$$A = \tfrac{1}{2} \times \tfrac{1}{2} = \tfrac{1}{4} \text{ sq in.}$$
$$s_u = ?$$

Substituting,

$$P = As$$
$$14,200 = \frac{1}{4}s$$
$$s = 56,800 \text{ psi} \qquad \text{ANS.}$$

PROBLEMS

1-37. A 1-in.-diam cast-iron bar failed under a compressive load of 75,000 lb.   Find its ultimate compressive strength.

1-38. A malleable cast-iron bar $1\frac{1}{8}$ by $2\frac{1}{4}$ in. in cross section failed under a tensile load of 81,000 lb.   Find its ultimate tensile strength.

1-39. What load would probably cause a $1\frac{7}{8}$-in.-diam cast-iron bar to fail in tension?   In compression?

1-40. A structural-steel test bar 1 in. diam failed under a compressive load of 96,000 lb.   What tensile load would probably cause it to fail?

1-41. Determine the compressive load which would probably cause a 2- by 4-in. timber post to fail.

1-42. A wrought-iron bar $\frac{3}{4}$ by $1\frac{1}{4}$ in. in cross section failed under a tensile load of 60,000 lb.   What is its ultimate strength?

1-11. Factor of Safety

As previously stated (Art. 1-7) a stress over the elastic limit of a material will produce a permanent set or deformation. A small number of repetitions of such a stress will usually cause failure.   It has also been found experimentally that, even though a stress is kept below the elastic limit, a large number of repetitions of such a stress may cause failure.   Such failure is called *fatigue* failure.   The maximum unit stress to which a material may be subjected repetitively an indefinite number of times without failure is a value somewhat below the elastic limit.

In order to avoid exceeding certain limiting values, a suitable factor of safety must be introduced.   The term *factor of safety* of a material, as commonly used, is the ratio of its ultimate strength to its working stress.   Algebraically this ratio may be expressed as

$$N = \frac{S_u}{S_w} \tag{1-7}$$

where N = factor of safety

S_u = ultimate strength, psi

S_w = working stress, psi

A considerable number of conditions determine the proper factor of safety to use. Some of these are:

1. *Material.* Obviously, steel would not require so large a factor of safety as timber.

2. *Uniformity of Material.* Defects such as knots, galls, and shakes in timber, or blowholes, pipes, and inclusions in steel will lower the ultimate strength.

3. Deterioration due to wear, corrosion, or other natural cause.

4. Damage which might occur if the material should fail. A workman might use a plank with a small factor of safety in a scaffold a few feet above the ground, but would demand an ample factor if failure meant a fall of 100 ft.

5. Possible overloading.

6. Method of applying the load.

7. The allowable working stress must always be below the elastic limit.

Table 1-5. *Factor of Safety*

MATERIAL	STEADY STRESS (BUILDINGS)	VARYING STRESS (BRIDGES)	REPEATED STRESS (MACHINES)
Structural steel	4	6	10
Wrought iron	4	6	10
Hard steel	6	8	15
Cast iron	6	10	20
Timber	8	10	15

Example 1-8.   A structural-steel plate with a cross section of $\frac{1}{2}$ by 24 in. is to be used under a steady stress condition.   Find the maximum compressive load it can sustain.

SOLUTION: Given

$$S_u = 60,000 \text{ psi} \qquad (\text{Table 1-4})$$
$$A = \frac{1}{2} \times 24 = 12 \text{ sq in.}$$
$$N = 4 \qquad (\text{Table 1-5})$$
$$S_w = ?$$
$$P = ?$$

Substituting,

$$N = \frac{S_u}{S_w}$$

$$4 = \frac{60,000}{S_w}$$

$$S_w = 15,000 \text{ psi}$$

Substituting,

$$P = As$$
$$P = 12 \times 15,000 = 180,000 \text{ lb} \qquad \text{ANS.}$$

PROBLEMS

1-43. What is the maximum safe load that a $1\frac{1}{2}$-in.-diam structural-steel rod can carry in tension when used under a steady stress condition?   When used in a bridge?   In a machine?   28000

1-44. The four corner timber posts of a platform sustain a total load of 80,000 lb.   Determine the size of square posts required.

1-45. In Prob. 1-44, what would have to be their diameter, if round?   5.045"

1-46. The four cast-iron legs of a machine sustain a maximum load of 10 tons.   Determine the diameter of legs required.

1-47. A wrought-iron rod is to support a tensile load of 50 tons.   Determine its diameter if used in a bridge.

1-48. A structural-steel rod is to be used under a tensile load of 40 tons.   Compute its diameter when used under a steady stress condition.

1-49. In Prob. 1-48, what should the diameter be if the rod is to be used in a bridge?

1-50. If the allowable stress for steel eyebars is 36,000 psi, how many bars 4½ by 1¼ in. will be required to carry a load of 450 tons? What will be the unit stress if each bar is stressed the same?

1-12. Stress-Strain Diagrams

The relation between the stress applied to a body and the resulting deformation or strain is shown graphically by means of the stress-strain diagram. By means of such diagrams, one can tell to what extent a body is changing in shape for each

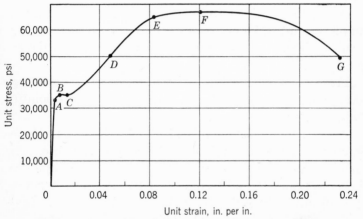

Fig. 1-4. Stress-strain diagram for medium steel in tension.

successive load from zero until the material actually breaks in two. The data for plotting a stress-strain diagram is obtained through tests made in material-testing laboratories.

Once the stress-strain diagram has been drawn for a test on a specific type of material, it is possible to apply this same diagram for all pieces of the same material that are alike metallurgically.

For example, Fig. 1-4 shows the stress-strain diagram for a medium steel bar in tension. The ordinates represent different values of the unit stress to which the test piece was subjected, and the abscissas represent the corresponding values of the unit deformation.

From the starting point (zero) to point *A*, the curve advances in a straight line, indicating that equal increases in the unit stress applied cause equal increases in the resulting strain.   In other words, unit strain is directly proportional to the unit stress applied.   The stress at point *A*, which is the last point on the straight line, is called the *elastic limit*, the highest unit stress which may be applied without a permanent set.

Above the elastic limit, the strain increases at a faster rate, until at point *B*, it continues with little or no increase in the load applied.   The unit stress at point *B* is called the *upper yield point*.

From point *B* to point *C*, the strain continues to increase even with a decrease in stress.   The unit stress at point *C* is called the *lower yield point*.

After the bar has passed the yield point, it begins to recover strength, so that for a further elongation it is necessary to increase the load, slowly at first, then more rapidly, as between *C* and *D*, and then more slowly again, as between *D* and *E*, until finally the elongation continues with no further increase in the load, as at *F*.   This load at *F* is the maximum load, and the unit stress at this load is called the *ultimate strength* of the material.

After the load has remained constant a short time at this maximum value, the additional elongation becomes localized and a neck is formed.   As the test progresses, this condition becomes aggravated and marks the point at which the test piece will sever, at a load somewhat less than the maximum, at point *G*.   This point is the point of rupture, and the unit stress is the *rupture strength* of the material.

The tension test diagram as shown in Fig. 1-4 is a typical stress-strain diagram.   Other materials will act in a similar manner. Mild steel, boiler-plate steel, and wrought iron, for instance, bear a very close resemblance to medium steel in their reactions to strain. Harder steels, such as high-carbon steel and certain alloys, have no yield point when tested in tension and break with much less elongation than mild

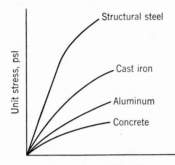

Fig. 1-5. Stress-strain comparison for several materials.

steel. Figure 1-5 shows a comparison of the stress-strain diagrams for several different materials in tension.

Compressive tests for steels give similar results.

1-13. Percentage of Elongation. Percentage of Reduction

In tensile tests, the test pieces continue to elongate, with a resulting reduction of cross-sectional area, as the test load is increased. This elongation and reduction of area are measures of the ductility of a metal. Ductility being a very important property of metals for certain uses, there are standard specifications, such as those of the American Society for Testing Materials (ASTM), which require a certain percentage of elongation as a minimum. Two standard gage lengths of materials have been adopted, an 8-in. length for rods, plates, and structural shapes, and a 2-in. length for forgings, castings, and other odd shapes.

Table 1-6 lists the per cent elongation for the 2-in. test

piece and the per cent reduction of area as specified by the ASTM for some of the more commonly used metals.

Table 1-6. *Per Cent Elongation and Reduction of Area*

MATERIAL	ELONGATION IN 2 IN., PER CENT	REDUCTION OF AREA, PER CENT
Structural steel	22	
Nickel steel	18	25
Wrought iron	40–45	40–45
Aluminum:		
Annealed	30–45	75–80
Cold-worked	18	65
Brass:		
Annealed	70	70
Cold-worked	15	60
Monel:		
Annealed	35–50	65–75
Cold-worked	35	45–75

In making the measurement for the computation of the percentage of elongation, the broken parts of the test piece are fitted together in the same relative position as before fracture and the new length is measured. The increase in length divided by the original length gives the relative elongation. This value multiplied by 100 gives the percentage of elongation.

Reduction of area is obtained from the difference between the original area of the cross section and the area of the cross section at the fracture. This difference in area divided by the original area gives the relative reduction of area. This value multiplied by 100 gives the percentage of reduction of area. It should be noted here that the final area used is not necessarily the area of the fracture, but of the smallest cross section at the neck.

Expressed in algebraic form, percentage of elongation is given as follows:

$$\text{Per cent } e = \frac{L_1 - L}{L} \times 100 \qquad (1\text{-}8)$$

where e = elongation, in.

$\quad L$ = original length, in.

$\quad L_1$ = final length, in.

Percentage of reduction of area is given by the following equation:

$$\text{Per cent } A_R = \frac{A - A_1}{A} \times 100 \qquad (1\text{-}9)$$

where A_R = reduction of area, sq in.

$\quad A$ = original area, sq in.

$\quad A_1$ = final area, sq. in.

Example 1-9.   Determine the percentage reduction of area and percentage elongation on a wrought-iron test piece, given the following data:

$$\begin{aligned}
&\text{Original diameter:} \quad 0.504 \text{ in.} \\
&\text{Final diameter:} \quad 0.289 \text{ in.} \\
&\text{Gage length:} \quad 2.000 \text{ in.} \\
&\text{Length after testing: } 2.860 \text{ in.}
\end{aligned}$$

Solution: Substituting in

$$\text{Per cent } e = \frac{L_1 - L}{L} \times 100$$

gives $\text{Per cent } e = \dfrac{2.860 - 2.000}{2.000} \times 100 = 43 \text{ per cent}$ ANS.

Before substituting in the equation for reduction of area, find the original and the final area:

$$A = \frac{\pi d^2}{4} = (0.7854)(0.504)^2 = 0.1995 \text{ sq in.}$$

$$A_1 = \frac{\pi d^2}{4} = (0.7854)(0.289)^2 = 0.0646 \text{ sq in.}$$

Substituting in

$$\text{Per cent } A_R = \frac{A - A_1}{A} \times 100$$

gives

$$\text{Per cent } A_R = \frac{0.1995 - 0.0646}{0.1955} \times 100 = 69 \text{ per cent} \quad \text{ANS.}$$

PROBLEMS

1-51. A nickel-steel test bar with a gage length of 2.005 in. and a diameter of 0.502 in. was stretched to a length of 2.422 in. after fracture. The minimum diameter at the fracture was 0.424 in. Find the percentage elongation and percentage reduction of area.

1-52. A structural-steel bar 0.751 in. diam with a gage length of 8 in. was tested in tension with the following results:

> Final gage length: 10.426 in.
> Diameter at rupture: 0.504 in.
> Load at elastic limit: 7,200 lb
> Maximum load: 14,600 lb

Compute elastic limit, ultimate strength, percentage elongation, percentage reduction of area.

1-53. A cold-worked monel metal test specimen 0.503 in. diam and 2 in. long reached its elastic limit under a tensile load of 17,700 lb and ruptured under a load of 19,750 lb. The final diameter was 0.412 in. and the final length 2.805 in. Compute elastic limit, ultimate strength, percentage elongation, percentage reduction of area. Does this test specimen meet ASTM requirements?

1-54. A wrought-iron test bar 0.751 in. diam held a tensile load of 24,600 lb as its maximum load. The original gage length of 8.005 in. was stretched to 11.212 in. Compute ultimate tensile strength and percentage elongation. Does this specimen meet ASTM requirements?

1-55. A structural-steel test bar 1.751 in. diam reached its elastic limit under a tensile load of 84,750 lb and ruptured under a load of 120,000 lb. Compute its elastic limit and ultimate strength. How does this specimen compare with the average structural-steel bar?

1-14. Ultimate Shearing Strength

When metal plates are to be cut to specified size and shape, or when holes are to be punched or drilled out of metal plates, the tools used to perform the operations must overcome the

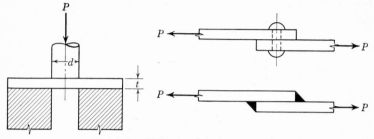

Fig. 1-6. Ultimate shearing strength.

ultimate shearing strength of the material to be cut. When two plates are welded or riveted together, the welds or rivets must be sufficiently strong to resist equal and oppositely directed forces P,P. In all cases, the total shearing force must be known in order to design properly for the existing conditions. If A_s is the area of the material in shear, and S_s is the ultimate shearing strength, the value of which may be found in tables, the ultimate shearing force P_s is given by the equation, $P_s = A_s S_s$.

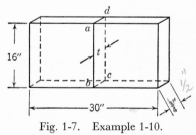

Fig. 1-7. Example 1-10.

Example 1-10. Determine the shearing force necessary to cut the structural-steel plate in two as shown in Fig. 1-7.

Solution: The area under shear is the area of the rectangle *abcd*, which is equal to the product of length *ab* and thickness *t*. Therefore

$$A_s = ab \times t = 16 \times \tfrac{1}{2} = 8 \text{ sq in.}$$
$$S_s = 50,000 \text{ psi}$$
$$P_s = ?$$

Substituting,

$$P_s = A_s S_s$$
$$P_s = 8 \times 50,000 = 400,000 \text{ lb} \qquad \text{ANS.}$$

Example 1-11. Determine the shearing force necessary to punch a 2-in.-diam hole in a mild steel plate $\frac{1}{2}$ in. thick.

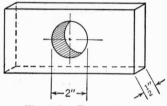

Fig. 1-8. Example 1-11.

SOLUTION: The area in shear equals the circumference of the hole times the thickness of the plate. Therefore

$$A_s = \pi dt = (3.1416)(2)(\tfrac{1}{2}) = 3.1416 \text{ sq in.}$$
$$S_s = 45,000 \text{ psi}$$
$$P_s = ?$$

Substituting,

$$P_s = A_s S_s$$
$$P_s = (3.1416)(45,000) = 141,000 \text{ lb} \qquad \text{ANS.}$$

Table 1-7 lists the values of ultimate shearing strength for some of the more commonly used materials.

Table 1-7. *Ultimate Shearing Strength, psi*

MATERIAL	ULTIMATE SHEARING STRENGH
Structural steel	50,000
Wrought iron	40,000
Malleable cast iron	40,000
Mild steel	45,000
Cast iron	25,000

$P = A s$

PROBLEMS

1-56. Determine the force required to punch a 1¾-in.-diam hole in a ¾-in. structural-steel plate.

1-57. What force is required to punch a ⅞-in.-diam hole in a wrought-iron plate ¾ in. thick?

1-58. If a force of 50,000 lb is required to punch a 1-in.-diam hole in a wrought-iron plate ⅜ in. thick, what is the ultimate shearing strength of the plate?

1-59. A mild steel plate 12 by 24 by ⅝ in. is to be cut into two square plates. Determine the shearing force on the cutting tool.

1-60. A cast-iron motor support is to have four holes in its base for mounting purposes. If the base is ¾ in. thick and the holes are clearance holes for 1-in. bolts, what is the shearing force to be overcome?

1-15. Temperature Stresses

Through ordinary ranges of temperature bodies expand as their temperature rises and contract as their temperature drops. The relative change in length per degree of temperature is called the *coefficient of linear expansion*. If the body is free to expand or contract with temperature changes, there will be no change in its condition of internal stress. Its change per unit length will vary directly as the change in temperature per degree. If the body is partly or wholly restrained so that it cannot expand or contract freely, the same internal stress will be set up as would be necessary to cause that same change in length. An increase in temperature will set up compressive stresses; a decrease, tensile stresses.

Stresses due to temperature changes should be avoided as much as possible by making suitable provision for parts to expand and contract freely. Thus, railroad rails, sidewalks, and pavements are laid with wide joints; pipelines are provided with expansion joints; bridges and roof trusses are equipped with rocker or roller bearings.

To express linear change and unit stress algebraically, if

C = coefficient of linear expansion

t = change in temperature, degrees

e = total change in length in any unit

L = length in same unit as e

s = unit stress, psi

E = modulus of elasticity, psi

ϵ = unit change in length

then the change in length of a body is expressed as

$$e = CtL \qquad (1\text{-}10)$$

and unit stress set up if the body is restrained as

$$s = CtE \qquad (1\text{-}11)$$

If e = total strain, and since unit strain $\epsilon = e/L$, by substituting equals for equals, we have

$$\epsilon = \frac{CtL}{L}$$

$$\epsilon = Ct \qquad (1\text{-}12)$$

Table 1-8 lists the coefficients of expansion for several of the more commonly used materials.

Table 1-8. *Coefficients of Linear Expansion*

MATERIAL	LINEAR EXPANSION $\times 10^{-6}$	
	FAHRENHEIT	CENTIGRADE
Aluminum	12.8	23.1
Brass	10.4	18.8
Bronze	10.1	18.1
Cast iron	5.9	10.6
Concrete	7.9	14.3
Copper	9.3	16.8
Steel	6.7	12.0
Wrought iron	6.7	12.0

Example 1-12.   New steel railroad rails were laid at a temperature of 50°F, with $\frac{1}{8}$-in. joints at each end.   The rails were 30 ft long. During the summer, the temperature rose to 110°F.   Determine the intensity and kind of stress developed.

SOLUTION: Given

$$C = 6.7 \times 10^{-6}$$
$$t = 60°$$
$$L = 30 \text{ ft} \times 12 = 360 \text{ in.}$$
$$E = 30,000,000 \text{ psi} = 3 \times 10^{7}$$
$$\epsilon = ?$$
$$e = ?$$
$$s = ?$$

Substituting,

$$\epsilon = Ct = (6.7 \times 10^{-6})60$$
$$\epsilon = 402 \times 10^{-6} = 0.000402 \text{ in. per in.} \quad \text{(unit strain)}$$

Total strain:

$$e = \epsilon L = (0.000402)360$$
$$e = 0.145 \text{ in.} \quad \text{(total strain or elongation)}$$

Since there is only 0.125-in. space between the rails,

$$e = 0.145 - 0.125 = 0.02\text{-in. compression}$$

Substituting,

$$s = \epsilon E = \frac{e}{L} E$$
$$s = \frac{(0.02)(3 \times 10^{7})}{360}$$
$$s = 1,670 \text{ psi} \quad \text{ANS.}$$

PROBLEMS

1-61. In Example 1-12, if the temperature drops to $-25°F$, how much allowance must be made in the length of the bolt slots to allow for proper contraction?

1-62. What will be the increase in length of a wrought-iron pipe 30 ft long which was set in place at 40°F if the temperature rises to 115°F?

X 1-63. A steel tape is exactly 100 ft long at 60°F. What will be its length at 95°F? At −20°F?

1-64. An annealed copper wire 3 ft long, rigidly held at both ends, is cooled 10°F. Find the intensity and kind of stress in the wire.

1-65. Determine the minimum length of joint necessary between railroad rails to prevent internal stress. Assume that the rails are 45 ft long and are laid at a temperature of 55°F and that the maximum temperature in that locality is 120°F.

1-66. A steel fence wire 0.157 in. diam is stretched between fixed posts with a tension of 100 lb when the temperature is 75°F. Determine the intensity and kind of stress developed when the temperature drops to −20°F.

X 1-67. A steel hoop makes a perfect fit around a wooden barrel of 6 ft OD when the temperature is 70°F. With a temperature drop to −20°F, determine the intensity and kind of stress developed, assuming that no change occurs in the diameter of the barrel. What is the inside diameter of the hoop at the latter temperature?

1-16. Statically Indeterminate Axially Loaded Members

If a body is constructed of more than one material, the equation of equilibrium, $P = As$, may not be sufficient to determine the stresses carried by the different parts of the body. In this case, the problem is statically indeterminate and requires additional equations for a solution. These additional equations are usually obtained from the relations between the elastic deformations in the component members.

Example 1-13. The short concrete post of Fig. 1-9 is reinforced with 6 steel rods ½ in. diam arranged in a circle of 12 in. diam. If the axially applied load is 100,000 lb, compute the stress developed in each material.

SOLUTION: From Fig. 1-9, the axially applied load must be balanced by the resisting forces on any perpendicular cross section. Thus,

$$P_S + P_C = 100,000$$

or
$$(As)_S + (As)_C = 100,000 \qquad (1\text{-}13)$$

In order to determine what proportion of the load is distributed to each material, we must consider the elastic deformation of the structure.

Due to the bearing plate, the steel rods and the concrete deform the same amount. Since both materials follow Hooke's law, we may write [see Eq. (1-6)]

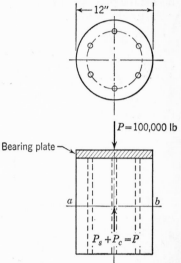

$$e_S = e_C$$

$$\left(\frac{PL}{AE}\right)_S = \left(\frac{PL}{AE}\right)_C$$

$$\left(\frac{sL}{E}\right)_S = \left(\frac{sL}{E}\right)_C$$

$$\left(\frac{s}{E}\right)_S = \left(\frac{s}{E}\right)_C$$

$$\frac{s_S}{s_C} = \frac{E_S}{E_C} \qquad (1\text{-}14)$$

Thus, in an axially loaded body of two materials of the same length, the unit stresses are directly proportional to their moduli of elasticity. From Table 1-3,

Fig. 1-9. Reinforced concrete post.

$$E_S = 30 \times 10^6 \qquad \text{and} \qquad E_C = 2 \times 10^6$$

Substituting in Eq. (1-14),

$$\frac{s_S}{s_C} = \frac{30 \times 10^6}{2 \times 10^6} = 15$$

$$s_S = 15s_C \qquad (1\text{-}15)$$

Thus, the unit stress in the steel is 15 times that in the concrete.

By solving Eq. (1-13) and (1-15) simultaneously,

$$A_S \times 15s_C + A_C \times s_C = 100,000$$

$$6\left(\frac{\pi}{4}\right)\left(\frac{1}{2}\right)^2 15s_C + \frac{\pi}{4}(12)^2 s_C = 100,000$$

$$17.6s_C + 113.1s_C = 100,000$$

$$s_C = 765 \text{ psi}$$

Since $s_S = 15s_C$,

$$s_S = 15 \times 765 = 11,500 \text{ psi}$$

Example 1-14. In Example 1-13, compute the total loads acting separately on the steel and the concrete.

36   *Simple Stresses*

SOLUTION: Since the amount of load carried by the individual members is the product of their respective cross-sectional areas and their unit stresses, we have

$$P_S = A_S \times s_S = 1.17 \times 11{,}500 = 13{,}500 \text{ lb}$$
$$P_C = A_C \times s_C = 113 \times 760 = 86{,}500 \text{ lb}$$

Check:

$$P = P_S + P_C = 13{,}500 + 86{,}500 = 100{,}000 \text{ lb}$$

Example 1-15.   A steel rod is placed inside a bronze tube, with the steel rod projecting 0.005 in. as shown in Fig. 1-10.   What is the maximum safe load P which may be applied to the bearing plate?

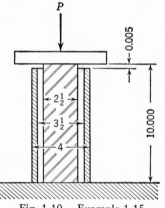

Fig. 1-10.   Example 1-15.

SOLUTION: Before the bronze tube can be stressed, the steel rod must deform (compress) 0.005 in.   Thus, the total deformation of the steel rod will be equal to the total deformation of the bronze tube plus 0.005 in.   Expressed as an equation,

$$e_s = e_b + 0.005$$

$$\left(\frac{sL}{E}\right)_s = \left(\frac{sL}{E}\right)_b + 0.005$$

$$\frac{s_S(10)}{30 \times 10^6} = \frac{s_b(10)}{12 \times 10^6} + \frac{5}{10^3}$$

$$s_S = \frac{30 \times 10^5}{12 \times 10^5}(s_b + 5 \times 12 \times 10^2)$$

$$s_S = 2.5 s_b + 15{,}000 \tag{1-16}$$

Equation (1-16) is the governing relation between the stresses. Substituting the working stress (Table 1-1) of 10,000 psi for bronze overstresses the steel to 40,000 psi. Therefore steel governs, and the allowable working stress in the bronze is found by using the working stress (Table 1-1) for steel of 20,000 psi.

$$20,000 = 2.5s_b + 15,000$$
$$s_b = 2,000 \text{ psi}$$

The maximum safe load is given by

$$P = P_S + P_b = (As)_S + (As)_b$$

$$P = \frac{\pi}{4}\left(\frac{25}{4}\right)20,000 + \frac{\pi}{4}\left(16 - \frac{49}{4}\right)2,000$$

$$P = \frac{\pi}{4}\left(\frac{25}{4} \times 20,000 + \frac{15}{4} \times 2,000\right)$$

$$P = 0.785(125,000 + 7,500)$$
$$P = 102,000 \text{ lb}$$

PROBLEMS

1-68. A short, hollow cast-iron cylinder is filled with concrete. If the outside diameter of the cylinder is 10 in. and its inside diameter is 8 in., compute the stress developed in each material by an axially applied load of 150,000 lb uniformly distributed over the cross section.

1-69. Compute the total deformation in Prob. 1-68 if the cylinder is 5 ft long.

1-70. A reinforced concrete column 12 in. diam and 10 ft long is subjected to an axial compressive load of 75,000 lb, which shortens the column by 0.02 in. Determine the stresses in the concrete and steel. Also calculate the cross-sectional areas of the concrete and steel.

1-71. A copper bar 2 in. diam is inserted into a steel shell 2.5 in. diam and 0.25 in. thick. What axial load will stretch the combined bar a total of 0.015 in. in a length of 5 ft?

1-72. A structural steel bar ½ by 2 in. by 5 ft long is placed between two brass bars of the same size. Compute the maximum compressive load the combined bar can carry and the total deformation.

1-73. A brass rod is placed inside a steel tube as shown in Fig. 1-11. Determine the maximum load P which may be applied to the bearing plate.

1-74. In Fig. 1-11, determine the maximum load P which may be applied if the rod is copper and the hollow tube is aluminum.

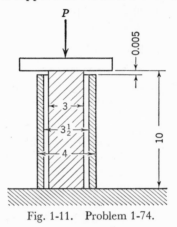

Fig. 1-11. Problem 1-74.

1-17. Mechanical Properties of Materials of Construction

The resistance which a material can offer to forces applied to it depends as much on its mechanical properties as on its shape and the manner of loading.

Materials of construction are classified as *metallic* or *nonmetallic*. The metallic materials are further classified as *ferrous* and *nonferrous*.

The ferrous metals are iron and its alloys, such as cast iron, malleable cast iron, wrought iron, and steel.

The nonferrous metals include aluminum, copper, magnesium, zinc, tin, lead, and the alloys which are produced by combining these elements, such as duralumin, brass, bronze, etc.

The nonmetallic materials include timber, stone, brick, concrete, plastics, rubber, glass, mica, leather, and asbestos.

The *mechanical properties* of materials are those properties

Know

which describe its behavior under mechanical usage, such as ductility, elasticity, hardness, toughness, and machinability. The determination of these and other mechanical properties is made in the testing laboratory under fixed rules of procedure. A knowledge of the mechanical properties of materials is essential in order to use them properly in design and construction.

Some of the most important mechanical properties of materials will now be discussed.

Ductility is the property of a material that enables it to be drawn out or elongated to an appreciable extent before rupture occurs. The percentage of elongation and of reduction of area are measures of the ductility of a material. Soft steel, wrought iron, copper, aluminum, and lead are examples of ductile materials.

Elasticity is the property that enables a material to return to its original shape and size upon the removal of the load which caused the deformation. All materials of construction are elastic, but the degree of elasticity varies greatly for different materials. Steel is a highly elastic material.

Plasticity is the property that enables the formation of a permanent deformation in a material. It is the direct opposite of elasticity, since a perfectly plastic body could have no elastic recovery. Gold and lead are metals which are highly plastic.

Malleability is the property of a material that permits it to be plastically compressed. Malleable materials may be hammered or rolled into any desired shape without rupture.

Brittleness is the absence of plasticity. Brittle materials are neither ductile nor malleable. They show very little deformation before rupturing, and then fail quite suddenly. Brittle materials do not have the capacity to be elongated plastically. Glass, stone, cast iron, and brick are brittle materials.

Hardness enables a material to resist abrasion or indentation. The diamond is among the hardest of materials.

Toughness is the property which enables a material to be twisted, bent, or stretched under a high stress before it ruptures.

Stiffness is the ability of a material to resist change in size and shape under a high stress.

Resilience is the property that enables a material to store energy and resist shock or impact. This property is important in situations where a member must resist moving bodies.

Machinability is the ease with which a material may be worked with cutting tools.

Corrosion resistance is the ability of a material to resist the destructive effects of corroding agents such as water and other chemicals.

1-18. The Determination of Mechanical Properties

In order to determine the mechanical properties of materials, test samples are subjected to appropriate tests in laboratories equipped for that purpose. These tests are made either to ascertain whether the properties of a given lot of the material meet the required standard for which that material is to be used, or to discover additional data concerning one or more of its properties. One of the simplest tests that can be made on most materials is the static tensile test. This test may be used to determine the ductility, elasticity, resilience, and many other properties of materials. Other tests commonly employed are compression, torsion, flexure, impact, fatigue, and cold-bending. The data of these tests are often shown graphically by the stress-strain diagram (see Art. 1-11).

1-19. The Ferrous Metals

All ferrous metals are made by refining pig iron and adding carbon and other elements to produce a desired combination of mechanical properties.

Cast iron is an alloy of iron and carbon that contains more than 1.7 per cent carbon. The carbon may be mixed with the iron mechanically in the form of graphite, or chemically in the form of iron carbide. Cast irons in which the carbon is mainly graphite are gray in color and so are called *gray cast irons*. They are extensively used for machine parts because they are inexpensive, can be given almost any desired form, are easily machined, and have high compressive strength. However, brittleness and lack of ductility and shock-resistance prohibit their use in parts subject to high tensile stresses or suddenly applied loads.

Alloys in which the carbon is in the form of iron carbide are referred to as *white cast irons* because they have a whitish appearance. White cast iron is used somewhat in parts which require abrasion resistance.

Malleable cast iron is white cast iron which is rendered malleable by proper annealing. Malleable iron is an inexpensive material tougher than gray iron and more resistant to bending and twisting. It is useful for many purposes, such as gear housings, brake pedals, tractor, and washing machine parts.

Wrought iron is a mechanical mixture of pig iron and a silicate slag. The hot and pasty mixture of iron and slag is compacted into rectangular blooms which are immediately rolled or hammered into bars or billets for further operation. It has excellent welding and forging qualities, and is quite tough and ductile. Before 1855, wrought iron was the most important metallic material used in construction. With the introduction of steel, the use of wrought iron greatly decreased, although it is still used extensively for pipes, pipe fittings, and culvert plates.

Steel is an alloy of iron and carbon in which the carbon content is less than 1.7 per cent. It is produced by oxidizing the impurities in molten pig iron and then adding the amount of carbon which will give the required combination of strength, ductility, and hardness properties. Since carbon is the element that controls the properties, these steels are called *carbon steels*. Carbon steels range from very low carbon steels (0.05 to 0.15 per cent carbon) to very high carbon steels (0.90 to 1.5 per cent carbon).

Alloy steels are steels to which elements other than carbon are added in sufficient amounts to produce special effects, such as greater resistance to corrosion, higher tensile strength, increased toughness, and hardness. The most common alloying metals are nickel, chromium, molybdenum, tungsten, vanadium, and silicomanganese. These alloy steels also include carbon in varying amounts, as well as very small amounts of phosphor, sulfur, and other impurities common to all iron products.

In general, alloy steels may be divided into four groups, namely, (1) structural steels, (2) machinery steels, (3) stainless steels, and (4) tool steels.

Alloy structural steels usually contain small amounts of alloying elements and less than 0.20 per cent carbon. They are used for structural purposes which require greater strength than can be obtained with carbon steel.

Alloy machinery steels usually contain less than 5 per cent of alloying elements. They are used primarily for machine parts and almost always in the heat-treated condition.

Stainless steels usually contain relatively large amounts of chromium (from 11 to 19 per cent) or nickel (from 12 to 36 per cent), or combinations of both. One of the latter is known as "18-8 stainless steel," since it has 18 per cent chromium and 8 per cent nickel. These steels are used mostly for corrosion resistance.

Alloy tool steels contain complex combinations of alloying elements and are used primarily for cutting tools and dies requiring special performance in the manufacture of materials.

There are so many different alloy steels on the market, that it is very difficult to make a selection that will satisfy all the requirements and, at the same time, be the least costly.   This often results in the use of an alloy steel where a good carbon steel would be just as satisfactory.   Present-day manufacturing methods have led to a better and more uniform carbon steel so that, more and more, carbon steel is replacing alloy steel in all types of construction.

1-20. The Nonferrous Metals

Metals and alloys of the nonferrous group have many properties which often make them more desirable to use than iron and steel.   They are more resistant to corrosion, and are, therefore, often used where ferrous metals would be damaged by corrosion.   They are lighter in weight, making them useful in places where weight is a deciding factor.   Some of them, such as copper and aluminum, are excellent conductors of electricity.

Pure aluminum is an extremely light (165 lb per cu ft) and ductile metal.   It can be rolled into thin sheets and fine wire. It is highly resistant to corrosion and has twice the electric conductivity of copper.   It is widely used for cooking utensils and electric cable and as an alloying metal.   Pure aluminum is not well adapted for structural purposes, because it is relatively soft and weak.   However, when other metals, such as copper, magnesium, manganese, and silicon, are added to aluminum, alloys are formed which compare favorably in strength and hardness with alloy steels.

Duralumin is an alloy of aluminum containing small percentages of copper, magnesium, and manganese.   Since it weighs only 174 lb per cu ft and has a high tensile strength, it is used extensively for structural forms for airplanes and other machines where weight is a deciding factor.

Aluminum bronze is an alloy containing approximately 10 per cent aluminum and 90 per cent copper. This alloy is highly resistant to corrosion in air and sea water, making it a valuable metal for naval use.

Copper is a very malleable and ductile metal with high electrical conductivity and corrosion resistance. These properties have led to its use for electric wiring, condenser tubes, and other conductors of electricity, as well as for roofing, hot-water tanks, and other places where corrosion resistance is of prime importance. About $\frac{1}{4}$ of the copper used in the United States is alloyed with zinc and tin to produce brasses and bronzes.

Brasses are alloys of copper and zinc, the most valuable of which are those containing between 60 to 90 per cent copper and 10 to 40 per cent zinc. Small percentages of other elements may be added to brasses to impart specific properties. For instance, tin will increase resistance to corrosion, and lead will improve machinability.

Bronzes are alloys of copper and tin, the most valuable of which are those containing between 75 to 95 per cent copper and 5 to 25 per cent tin. Bronzes have good strength and excellent resistance to wear and corrosion. The addition of lead improves the lubricating properties, making these alloys suitable for bushing. Phosphor bronze contains about 90 per cent copper, 10 per cent tin, 9 per cent lead, and 1 per cent phosphor. It can be wrought into wire and cast into gears, bearings, and other parts subjected to heavy pressures and high speeds.

1-21. Nonmetallic Materials

An important group of materials for construction is the so-called nonmetallic group. Stone, brick, and concrete are used for bridge piers and retaining walls. Timber is used for structural purposes in buildings, bridges, and trestles and for posts, poles, and ties. Plastics are used for such diverse articles as tires, gears, watch crystals, parachutes, and clothing.

The *stones* that find the greatest use in structures are granite, trap rock, limestone, marble, sandstone, and slate. The properties of stone and brick are far more variable than similar properties of metals. Therefore, very high factors of safety must be used in determining safe working stresses.

Concrete is a mixture of portland cement, sand, gravel or broken stone, and water. The most important factors influencing the strength of concrete are the quality and proportion of cement, the ratio of water to cement, and workmanship in mixing and placing.

Reinforced concrete is concrete combined with steel in the form of twisted or deformed rods which provide uneven surfaces. Reinforced concrete is used in structures where high tensile strength is required.

Structural timber is made mostly from the coniferous or needle-leaved trees which are considered softwoods. The hardwoods of the broad-leaved trees are used very rarely for large structural timbers. Many factors influence the mechanical properties of timber, the most important being density, moisture content, and defects. Knots, shakes, and galls are the most common defects of timber.

Plastics is a term applied to a large class of moldable organic compounds. There are countless different kinds sold under hundreds of different trade names, with new kinds and new uses being discovered constantly. Plastics are competing with and displacing wood, leather, glass, rubber, and even metals in such articles as clock cases, steering wheels, radio cabinets, instrument panels, tubes for oil and water, shatterproof crystals, and automobile tires.

Plastics are divided roughly into two classes, called *thermoplastics* and *thermosetting plastics*. Materials in the thermoplastic group become soft and pliable when they are heated to moderate temperatures, and then harden when cooled. They will soften every time heat is applied and can be reheated and reworked as often as desired. Thermosetting plastics will soften the first time they are heated and then harden when cooled, but once set, they cannot again be softened by reheating. Plastics can be molded, extruded, cast, or folded into sheets.

Natural rubber is a soft and tacky material which deteriorates very rapidly when exposed to air and sunlight and becomes hard and brittle when cold. Its properties are improved by the process of vulcanization. Because of the large deformation which it will take before breaking, soft rubber is a very useful material for buffers and shock absorbers. Its low electrical conductivity makes it useful as insulating materials.

Synthetic rubbers, or rubber substitutes, are made from plastics such as ethyl cellulose and some of the polyvinyl resins. None of them has proved to be equal to rubber in tensile and mechanical strength, elongation, and resiliency. However, they are superior to rubber in resistance to heat and to deterioration when exposed to air and sunlight and also in the presence of oils and other organic solvents. These properties enable synthetic rubber to be used for truck and automobile tires, inner tubes, oil and gas hose, gaskets, and tank linings.

2: Riveted and Welded Joints

RIVETED JOINTS

2-1. Types of Joints—Definitions

There are two methods of joining structural members together, namely, by rivets or by welds. There are two types of riveted joints in general use: lap joints and butt joints.

In a lap joint, the plates to be connected are overlapped and joined together by one or more rows of rivets (Fig. 2-1). If the joint has one row of rivets, it is called a *single-riveted lap joint;* two rows, *double-riveted*, etc.

A lap joint may be in *single* or *double* shear, according to whether one or two cross-sectional areas of rivets may be sheared.

In a butt joint, the two plates are placed end to end and fastened together by two cover plates, or by butt straps, riveted to each of the main plates.

A butt joint is always in double shear, since two cross-sectional rivet areas will be sheared. Butt joints are identified as single-riveted, double-riveted, and so forth, according to the number of rows of rivets located on one side of the joint.

In general, lap joints are used when the plates to be riveted together are not over $\frac{1}{2}$ in. thick. Plates which exceed $\frac{1}{2}$-in.

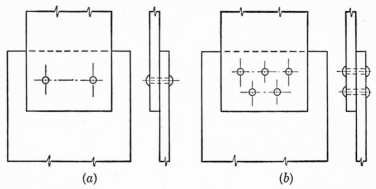

Fig. 2-1. Lap joints. (*a*) Single-riveted lap joint. (*b*) Double-riveted lap joint.

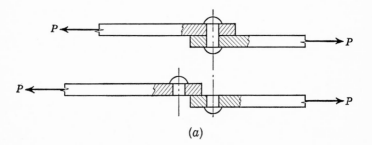

(*a*)

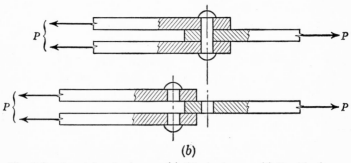

(*b*)

Fig. 2-2. Lap joints in shear. (*a*) Single shear. (*b*) Double shear.

thickness undergo an excessive bending action in a lap joint and therefore are usually fastened together in a butt joint.

The center-to-center distance between two adjacent rivets in any row is called the pitch (P). The pitch may or may not

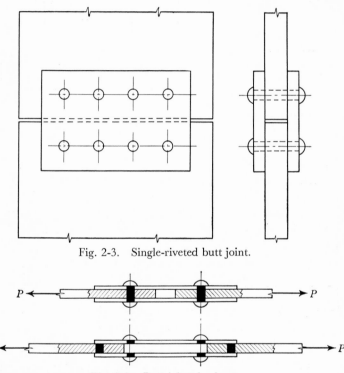

Fig. 2-3. Single-riveted butt joint.

Fig. 2-4. Butt joints in shear.

be the same for every row, as shown in Fig. 2-5. The distance between two adjacent rows of rivets is called the *transverse pitch* (P_t). The diagonal distance between adjacent rivets on adjoining rows, when the rivets are staggered, is called the *diagonal pitch* (P_d).

In calculating the strength of a long-riveted joint, it often is convenient to use a length of joint which corresponds to a repeating pattern of rivets. This eliminates the necessity of considering all the rivets in the joint. This length of joint is called a *repeating section*. In Fig. 2-5, the repeating section is shown crosshatched to show more clearly how many rivets belong to a repeating section. A study of this section shows

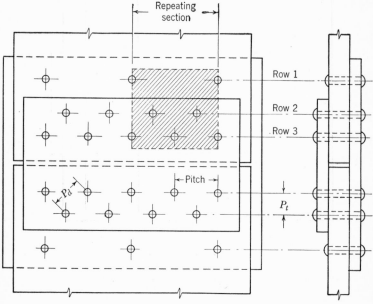

Fig. 2-5. Pitch and repeating section.

that there are five rivets: two half-rivets in row 1, two whole rivets in row 2, and one whole and two half-rivets in row 3.

2-2. Assumptions in the Design of Riveted Joints

A basic assumption in the design of riveted joints is that the load is distributed equally among the rivets. The resultant of the resisting forces will then pass through the centroid of the rivet group. If the applied load also passes through this centroid, there will be no eccentricity. Actually, this is an approximation which only approaches the assumed condition after the rivets have been loaded and the stresses relieved. This is one of the reasons for the codes specifying the allowable stresses for riveted joints (see Art. 2-4).

Another assumption is that there will be no bending action in the rivet, thereby allowing the use of the basic stress formula, $s = P/A$. However, excessive stresses could develop because of bending if rivets with relatively long grips must be used. Here again, the several technical societies avert the danger of excessive bending stresses by increasing the number of rivets whenever the grip exceeds $4\frac{1}{2}$ times the diameter of the rivet.

2-3. Types of Stress

Riveted joints afford an excellent illustration of tension, compression, and shear and of the manner of transmission of

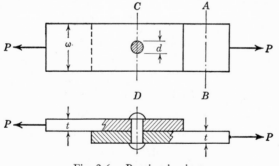

Fig. 2-6. Bearing in rivet.

stress. If two plates are held together by a rivet as shown in Fig. 2-6, and a tensile load P applied, the force is transmitted from one plate to the other through the rivet. Let w = width of plate, t = its thickness, d = diameter of the rivet. The unit tensile stress in section AB is $s = P/A = P/wt$. At section CD through the rivet hole, the cross-sectional area is $(w - d)t$ and the unit tensile stress in the net area is $s = P/(w - d)t$. For determining tension in plate, it is customary to add ⅛ in. to the diameter of the rivet to allow for rivet expansion and possible damage at the circumference of the hole.   If there is a total of n rivets at section CD, the cross-sectional area of the plate in tension is $[w - (d + \frac{1}{8})n]t$ and the unit tensile stress become $s = P/[w - (d + \frac{1}{8})n]t$.

The addition of one or more rows of rivets will have no effect on the tension in plate unless there is a different number of rivets in the additional rows.   In the latter case, the maximum unit tensile stress would be determined from the row with the largest number of rivets (see Fig. 2-7).

At the cross section of the rivet between the two plates, (Fig. 2-6), the force from one plate is transmitted to the other

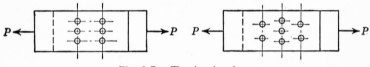

Fig. 2-7.   Tension in plate.

by means of shear in the rivet.   Assuming the unit stress to be uniformly distributed over the cross section, the unit stress in shear in rivet is $s = P/A = 4P/\pi d^2$.   Again, if there is a total of n rivets in the joint, the unit stress in shear is $s = 4P/\pi d^2 n$.   In the case of double shear, since there are two cross-sectional areas of rivets in shear,

$$s = \frac{4P}{2\pi d^2 n} = \frac{2P}{\pi d^2 n}$$

On the right side of the rivet in the upper plate, and on the opposite side in the lower plate (Fig. 2-6), force is transmitted from the plate to the rivet in compression or bearing.   Assuming that the rivet fills the hole, the unit intensity of the bearing stress cannot exceed the amount that it would be if the total pressure were acting upon the projected area dt.   Therefore the unit stress in bearing on the rivet is $s = P/dt$.   Once more, if there is a total of n rivets in the joint and each rivet is assumed to carry an equal amount of the load, then $s = P/dtn$.

Finally, there is a shearing stress in the plate, as shown in Fig. 2-8. Since the plate is sheared along two sides, the area in shear in plate would be $A = 2$ ft, where $f =$ distance from the rivet to the edge of the plate. The unit stress in shear in plate is $s = P/2ft$. A total of n rivets in the plate will make the unit stress in shear $s = P/2ftn$.

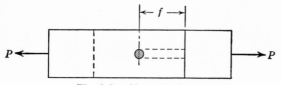

Fig. 2-8. Shear in plate.

Then, for the four possible failures that may occur in a riveted joint, we may use the following equations:

1. Shear in rivet:

$$s = \frac{4P}{\pi d^2 n} \qquad P = \frac{\pi d^2 ns}{4}$$

NOTE: In case of double shear, multiply area by 2.

2. Bearing in rivet:

$$s = \frac{P}{dtn} \qquad P = dtns$$

3. Tension in plate:

$$s = \frac{P}{[w - (d + \frac{1}{8})n_1]t} \qquad P = [w - (d + \frac{1}{8})n_1]ts$$

NOTE: $n_1 =$ maximum number of rivets in one row.

4. Shear in plate:

$$s = \frac{P}{2ftn} \qquad P = 2ftns$$

where $n =$ total number of rivets in joint

  $t =$ thickness of plate, in.

  $f =$ edge distance, in.

  $w =$ width of plate, in.

d = diameter of rivet, in.
P = external load, lb
s = unit stress, psi

2-4. Allowable Stresses

There are several technical agencies which, through the years, have formulated specific and detailed rules governing the design and fabrication of riveted joints. These rules have been included in codes, of which the most familiar are (1) the American Institute of Steel Construction (AISC) code for buildings, (2) the American Society of Mechanical Engineers (ASME) Boiler Code, and (3) the American Railway Engineering Association (AREA) code for railway bridges.

In Table 2-1 are shown the allowable unit stresses in shear and bearing in rivet, and tension and shear in plate given by the three societies listed above.

An analysis of these three codes, shows several differences among them, indicating the safety factor deemed necessary for the particular riveted joints to which they apply.

There are several differences among the various codes in the use of the formulas for calculation of rivet strength. For example, in determining *shear and bearing in rivet*, the AISC

Table 2-1. *Allowable Stresses for Riveted Joints, psi*

	SHEAR IN RIVET	BEARING IN RIVET	TENSION IN PLATE	SHEAR IN PLATE
AISC for buildings	15,000	32,000 (single shear) 40,000 (double shear)	20,000	15,000
AREA for railroad bridges:				
Power-driven rivets	13,500	27,000	18,000	13,500
Hand-driven rivets	11,000	20,000	18,000	11,000
ASME for boilers	8,800	19,000	11,000	8,800

and AREA use the nominal size of the rivet for obtaining the area in question; the ASME uses the diameter of the rivet holes (usually $\frac{1}{16}$ in. larger than the rivet), equivalent to the diameter of the rivet in expanded state after driving.

In *tension in plate*, the AISC and AREA deduct rivet diameter plus $\frac{1}{8}$ in. for punched holes, and rivet diameter plus $\frac{1}{16}$ in. for punched and reamed holes; ASME deducts diameter of rivet hole.

To determine the safe load that a riveted joint may carry, the load for each stress must be calculated. The smallest calculated load determines the safe load.

To determine if a given load is safe, the unit stress for each type of strain must be calculated. If each is within the specifications for allowable unit stress, the load is safe.

2-5. Rivet Spacing

AISC specifications for the minimum center-to-center distance between rivets is that this pitch distance be three times the diameter of the rivet. For the edge distance from the center of the rivet to the edge of the plate, one and one-half times the diameter of the rivet (or one-half the pitch distance) is the usual requirement.

Example 2-1. Determine the safe load of the lap joint shown in Fig. 2-9.

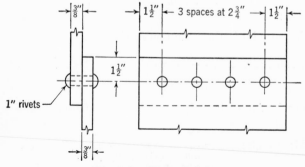

Fig. 2-9. Example 2-1.

56   *Riveted and Welded Joints*

SOLUTION:

1. Shear in rivet:
$$P = \frac{\pi d^2 n s}{4} = \frac{(3.1416)(1)^2(4)(15,000)}{4}$$
$$P = 47,125 \text{ lb}$$

2. Bearing:
$$P = dtns = (1)(\tfrac{3}{8})(4)(32,000)$$
$$P = 48,000 \text{ lb}$$

3. Tension in plate:
$$P = [w - (d + \tfrac{1}{8})n_1]ts$$
$$P = [11\tfrac{1}{4} - (1 + \tfrac{1}{8})4](\tfrac{3}{8})(20,000)$$
$$P = 50,675 \text{ lb} \quad 50,625$$

4. Shear in plate:
$$P = 2ftns = (2)(1\tfrac{1}{2})(\tfrac{3}{8})(4)(15,000)$$
$$P = 67,500 \text{ lb}$$

The safe load is 47,125 lb and the joint fails in shear in rivet.

Example 2-2.   Compute the unit stresses in the butt joint in Fig. 2-10 if the working load is to be 90,000 lb.

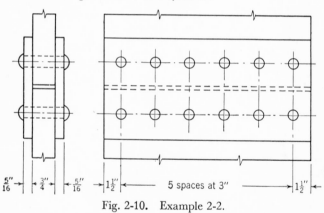

$\frac{5''}{16} \quad \frac{3''}{4} \quad \frac{5''}{16} \quad 1\frac{1}{2}'' \quad$ 5 spaces at 3'' $\quad 1\frac{1}{2}''$

Fig. 2-10.   Example 2-2.

SOLUTION:

1. A butt joint is always in double shear.

   Shear in rivet:
   $$s = \frac{2P}{\pi d^2 n} = \frac{(2)(90,000)}{(3.1416)(1)^2(6)}$$
   $$s = 9,550 \text{ psi}$$

2. Bearing: must be calculated for main plate and also for butt straps.

   Main plate:
   $$s = \frac{P}{dtn} = \frac{90,000}{(1)(\tfrac{3}{4})(6)}$$
   $$s = 20,000 \text{ psi}$$

Butt straps: total area in bearing is $A = 2 \times \frac{5}{16} \times 1 \times 6$

$$s = \frac{P}{dtn} = \frac{90,000}{(2)(\frac{5}{16})(1)(6)}$$

$$s = 24,000 \text{ psi}$$

3. Tension in plate:

Main plate: $\quad s = \dfrac{P}{[w - (d + \frac{1}{8})n_1]t} = \dfrac{90,000}{[18 - (1 + \frac{1}{8})6]\frac{3}{4}}$

Butt straps: $\quad s = \dfrac{P}{[w - (d + \frac{1}{8})n_1]t}$

$$= \dfrac{90,000}{[18 - (1 + \frac{1}{8})6]2 \times \frac{5}{16}}$$

$$s = 12,800 \text{ psi}$$

4. Shear in plate:

Main plate: $\quad s = \dfrac{P}{2ftn} = \dfrac{90,000}{2(1\frac{1}{2})(\frac{3}{4})6}$

$$s = 6,670 \text{ psi}$$

Butt straps: $\quad s = \dfrac{P}{2ftn} = \dfrac{90,000}{2(1\frac{1}{2})(2 \times \frac{5}{16})6}$

$$s = 8,000 \text{ psi}$$

Therefore all stresses are within AISC specifications, and the load is safe.

PROBLEMS

2-1. Determine the safe load which can be carried by the lap joint in Fig. 2-11.

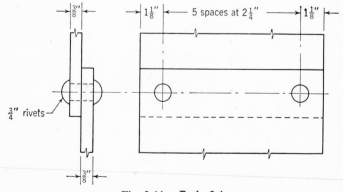

Fig. 2-11. **Prob.** 2-1.

2-2. Determine the safe load which can be carried by the lap joint in Fig. 2-12.

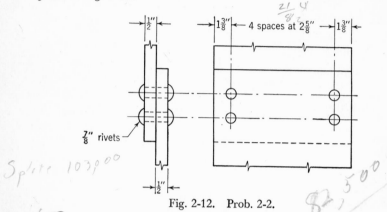

Fig. 2-12.   Prob. 2-2.

2-3. Compute the unit stresses developed in the lap joint of Fig. 2-13.   The working load is 140,000 lb.   Is the joint safe?

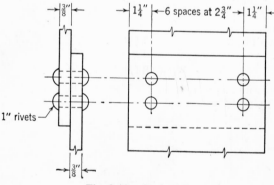

Fig. 2-13.   Prob. 2-3.

2-4. What is the maximum allowable load which can be carried by the butt joint in Fig. 2-14?

2-5. Compute the unit stresses developed in a butt joint 21 in. wide, using 1-in.-diam rivets in a double row spaced 3 in. apart. The plates are $\frac{3}{4}$ in. thick, the butt straps $\frac{5}{16}$ in. thick, and the working load 100,000 lb.   Is the joint safe?

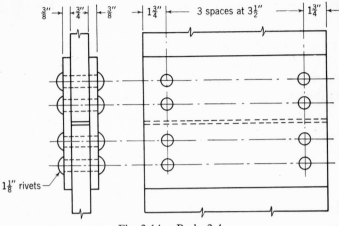

Fig. 2-14. Prob. 2-4.

2-6. Efficiency of a Riveted Joint

The efficiency of a riveted joint is the ratio of the least strength of the joint to the strength of the unpunched plate in tension. Obviously, the over-all efficiency of a riveted joint can never reach 100 per cent, since the joint cannot be made as strong as the unpunched or undrilled plate. The efficiencies of the various standard-type joints range from around 50 to 63 per cent for single-riveted lap joints to as high as 94 per cent for some of the butt joints used in large high-pressure boilers and tanks. To compute the efficiency of a joint, the load for each type of stress must be computed. The smallest load determines the safe load. Since the safe load that can be carried by an unpunched plate is $P = As$, then

$$\text{Efficiency} = \frac{P_s}{P} \times 100 \qquad \text{per cent}$$

where P_s = safe load of riveted joint
P = safe load of unpunched plate

Example 2-3.   Determine the efficiency of the lap joint in Fig. 2-9.

Solution: The safe load as previously calculated was 47,125 lb. The safe load that can be carried by the unpunched plate is

$$P = As = (11\tfrac{1}{4})(\tfrac{3}{8})(20,000)$$
$$P = 84,375 \text{ lb}$$

Substituting,

$$\text{Efficiency} = \frac{P_s}{P} \times 100 \qquad \text{per cent}$$

$$\text{Efficiency} = \frac{47,125}{84,375} \times 100 = 56 \text{ per cent} \qquad \text{ANS.}$$

PROBLEMS

2-6.   Determine the efficiency of the lap joint in Fig. 2-11.

2-7.   Determine the efficiency of the lap joint in Fig. 2-12.

2-8.   Determine the efficiency of the butt joint in Fig. 2-13.

2-9.   Compute the efficiency of a riveted lap joint using six $\tfrac{3}{4}$-in. rivets in a single row.   The pitch distance is $2\tfrac{1}{2}$ in.; the edge distance is $1\tfrac{1}{8}$ in.   The plates are $\tfrac{1}{2}$ in. thick.

2-10.   Compute the efficiency of a butt joint using twelve $\tfrac{7}{8}$-in. rivets in a double row.   The rivets are spaced 3 in. apart; the edge distance is $1\tfrac{1}{2}$ in.   The plates are $\tfrac{3}{4}$ in. thick, and the butt straps $\tfrac{5}{16}$ in. thick.   Where will the joint fail?

2-7. Design of Riveted Joints

In designing a riveted joint, the allowable unit stresses are either given or assumed as the AISC maximum specification. The first step is to determine the number of rivets necessary to carry the load in shear.

With the size and number of rivets determined, the thickness of plate necessary to carry the load in compression or bearing may be computed next.   If the plate is excessively thick, a larger number of smaller rivets may be used.

After the thickness of plate has been determined, the width of plate necessary to carry the load in tension may be computed.

The minimum pitch distance for rivets is usually three times the diameter of the rivet, and the minimum edge distance one and one-half times the rivet diameter.

Example 2-4.   Design a lap joint to carry a load of 75,000 lb. The rivets are $\frac{3}{4}$ in. diam and placed in a double row.   Draw a shop sketch for the lap joint.

SOLUTION:

1. Shear-in-rivet formula: $s = \dfrac{4P}{\pi d^2 n}$

   Solve for n:
   $$n = \frac{4P}{\pi d^2 s} = \frac{(4)(75,000)}{(3.1416)(\frac{3}{4})^2(15,000)}$$
   $$n = 11.3$$

   Twelve rivets will be required.

2. Bearing-in-rivet formula: $s = \dfrac{P}{dtn}$

   Solve for t:
   $$t = \frac{P}{dns} = \frac{75,000}{\frac{3}{4}(12)(32,000)}$$
   $$t = 0.261$$

   Commercial thicknesses are in increments of sixteenths; therefore plate thickness will be $\frac{5}{16}$ in.

3. Tension in plate formula:
   $$s = \frac{P}{[w - (d + \frac{1}{8})n_1]t}$$
   Solve for w:
   $$w = \frac{P}{ts} + \left(d + \frac{1}{8}\right)n_1$$
   $$w = \frac{75,000}{(\frac{5}{16})(20,000)} + \left(\frac{3}{4} + \frac{1}{8}\right)6 = 17\frac{1}{4} \text{ in.}$$

4. Since there are six rivets in each row, there will be five spaces between rivets plus two edge distances, a total of six spaces. Therefore

   $$17\frac{1}{4} \div 6 = 2\frac{7}{8}\text{-in. pitch distance}$$
   $$\frac{1}{2} \times 2\frac{7}{8} = 1\frac{7}{16}\text{-in. edge distance}$$

5. *Check:* AISC specifications for minimum distance between rivets is three times the diameter of the rivet.

$$3 \times \tfrac{3}{4} = 2\tfrac{1}{4} \text{ in.}$$

Therefore requirement is met. AISC specification for minimum edge distance is one and one-half times the diameter of the rivet.

$$1\tfrac{1}{2} \times \tfrac{3}{4} = 1\tfrac{1}{8} \text{ in.}$$

Therefore requirement is met.

6. Shop sketch.

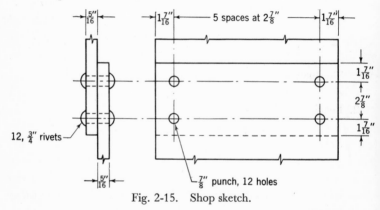

Fig. 2-15. Shop sketch.

PROBLEMS

2-11. Design a lap joint to carry a load of 45,000 lb, using $\tfrac{3}{4}$-in. rivets in a single row. Draw the shop sketch.

2-12. Design a lap joint to carry a load of 90,000 lb, using $\tfrac{7}{8}$-in. rivets in a double row. Make a shop sketch.

2-13. Design a butt joint to carry a load of 100,000 lb, using $\tfrac{3}{4}$-in. rivets in a single row. Make a shop sketch.

2-14. Design a butt joint to carry a load of 160,000 lb, using $\tfrac{7}{8}$-in. rivets in a double row.

2-15. Design a lap joint and draw the shop sketch for the following data: load, 60,000 lb; rivets, $\tfrac{7}{8}$ in. diam; plate width, 19 in.

2-16. Design a butt joint and draw the shop sketch given the following data: load, 150,000 lb; rivets, $\tfrac{3}{4}$ in. diam; plate width, 18 in.

WELDED JOINTS

2-8. Welding

The process of welding may be defined as the joining of two pieces of metal by the application of heat.   There are two common methods of welding—fusion welding and pressure welding.   Fusion welding is the process of joining two pieces of metal in the molten state without the application of mechanical pressure or blows.   The heat for fusion welding is supplied in several different ways, the most common being gas (oxyacetylene), electric arc, and chemical (thermite).

Pressure welding is the process of joining two pieces of metal by heating them to a plastic state and then forcing them together by mechanical pressure or blows.

Fusion welding, or the nonpressure method, is the preferred method of welding.

The heat applied to a welded joint tends to change the properties of the surrounding metal, thereby setting up internal stresses.   In some instances it is necessary to heat-treat in order to relieve the internal stresses set up during the welding process.   This treatment consists of a gradual heating of the entire weld or of the whole member to a temperature somewhat below the lower critical temperature of the metal and then cooling it slowly.

Welding is now being more widely used than ever before in making connections which previously were always riveted, especially in the automobile, railroad-car, and airplane industries.

2-9. Types of Welded Joints

The most important of the various types of welded joints in common use are (1) fillet welds, (2) butt welds, (3) spot welds, and (4) tack welds.

A *fillet weld* is one placed in a corner made by two adjoining members. Fillet welds are generally made with equal legs so that the length of these legs is used to represent the size of the fillet weld.

A *butt weld* is obtained by butting together the edges of two pieces having practically the same cross section and heating until fused together.

Spot welds are made by the simultaneous application of intense pressure to and high current through the two metal pieces at the point where they are to be joined. The current creates extreme heat, which causes the metal in both pieces to melt and merge with each other. Upon air-cooling, the two pieces are securely joined.

Tack welds are used for holding metal parts in position while the major welding operation is in progress.

2-10. Fillet Welds

Most welds used in structural work are of the fillet type. Fig. 2-16 shows a fillet weld, which forms a right-angled

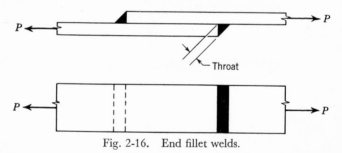

Fig. 2-16. End fillet welds.

triangle. The smallest distance (altitude) from the right angle to the hypotenuse is called the *throat*. The fillet weld illustrated in Fig. 2-16 is called an *end weld*. If the weld is deposited along the sides of the parts to be connected (see Fig. 2-17), it is called a *side weld*. If the two parts are welded together along the sides and also on the ends, it is called a *combination weld* (see Fig. 2-18).

In fillet welding, the fillet resists the slipping of one plate relative to the other, and, consequently, shear stresses are set up in the metal of the fillets. The least cross-sectional area of the weld, and therefore the plane of maximum stress, is through the throat of the weld. Thus the strength of the weld is proportional to the throat area, the throat area being the product of the throat width and the total length of weld.

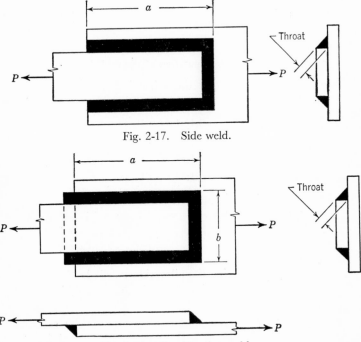

Fig. 2-17. Side weld.

Fig. 2-18. Combination welds.

The American Welding Society (AWS) recommends 11,300 psi as the allowable shearing stress for 45° fillet welds. The allowable load per linear inch of fillet is computed as follows: In Fig. 2-19, both legs of the weld are ½ in. as indicated. The throat of the weld is $0.707 \times 0.5 = 0.3535$ in. The shearing strength per linear inch of weld will be

$$1 \times 0.3535 \times 11,300 = 3,995 \text{ lb}$$

or 4,000 lb.

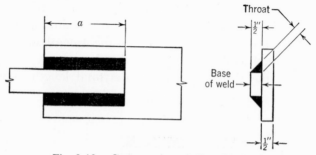

Fig. 2-19.   Computation of allowable load.

The AWS Codes specify the following allowable loads per linear inch of fillet:

⅛-in. base of weld: 1,000 lb per linear in.
¼-in. base of weld: 2,000 lb per linear in.
⅜-in. base of weld: 3,000 lb per linear in.
½-in. base of weld: 4,000 lb per linear in.

From these values, it may be observed that the strength of a fillet weld is 1,000 lb per linear in. of weld for each ⅛ in. of base.   Base widths not given in the above table may be derived by interpolation.

Example 2-5.   Determine the allowable tensile load of two ½-in. steel plates which are joined together by a fillet weld.   The total length of weld is 16 in.

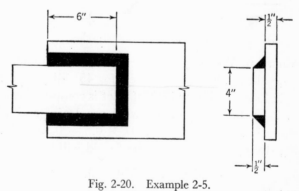

Fig. 2-20.   Example 2-5.

SOLUTION: The plate thickness is ½ in.; therefore the base of weld is ½ in. Allowable load will be 4,000 lb per lin in. of weld. Length of weld is 16 in. Therefore

$$P = 4,000 \times 16 = 64,000 \text{ lb} \qquad \text{ANS.}$$

PROBLEMS

2-17. Two ⅜-in steel plates are joined in a side weld as shown in Fig. 2-21. What must be the total length of weld to support a load of 48,000 lb?

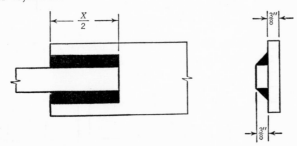

Fig. 2-21. Prob. 2-17.

2-18. A 4- by ½-in. steel plate is fastened to a 6- by ½-in. steel plate by means of fillet welds. What is the safe load if welded on the sides only? What is the safe load if the weld is run also across both ends of the plates (see Fig. 2-22)?

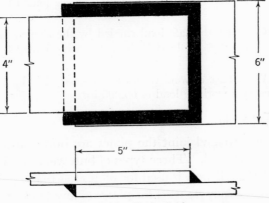

Fig. 2-22. Prob. 2-18.

2-19. Two 6- by ½-in. steel plates are joined with end welds as shown in Fig. 2-23. Calculate the allowable load for the joint, assuming each weld transmits one-half the load.

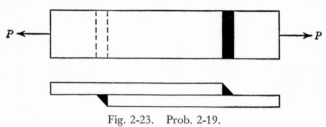

Fig. 2-23.   Prob. 2-19.

2-20. Calculate the base (*b*) of weld necessary in Fig. 2-24 in order for the joint to carry a working load of 40,000 lb.

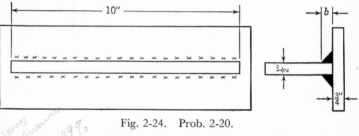

Fig. 2-24.   Prob. 2-20.

2-21. Compare the safe load carried by the riveted lap joint in Fig. 2-11 with the safe load if the plates were joined by two end welds.

2-22. Compare the safe load carried by the riveted lap joint in Fig. 2-12 with the safe load if the plates were joined by two end welds.

2-23. What base of weld would be necessary in Fig. 2-24 for the joint to carry a working load of 60,000 lb?

2-11. Butt Welds

In a butt-welded joint the plates are butted together and their edges welded.   Three types of butt welds are illustrated in Fig. 2-25.   Type *a* is used for plates less than ⁵⁄₁₆ in. thick; types *b* and *c* may be used for plates of any thickness.   In no case should there be a large amount of excess material at the top or bottom of the weld. The reinforcement should curve gradually into the plate and be finished smoothly in order to avoid a large stress concentration at the weld.

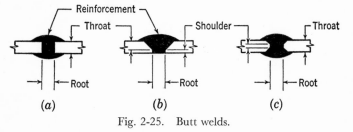

Fig. 2-25. Butt welds.

The AWS gives the following allowable unit stresses for butt joints in tension and compression:

Tension on section through throat of weld: 13,000 psi
Compression on section through throat of weld: 18,000 psi

Problems involving butt joints are similar to those involving lap joints with the exception of the lower allowable value in tension.

Example 2-6. Determine the allowable load in tension of two 10- by ¾-in. steel plates which are butt-welded together.

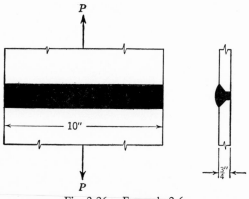

Fig. 2-26. Example 2-6.

SOLUTION: If P_t = allowable tensile load

A = cross-sectional area of weld

s_t = allowable tensile stress

$$P_t = As_t = (10 \times \frac{3}{4})(13,000)$$
$$P_t = 97,500 \text{ lb} \quad \text{ANS.}$$

PROBLEMS

2-24. Determine the allowable tensile load of a butt-welded joint between two plates 12 by $\frac{1}{2}$ in.

2-25. What would be the allowable compressive load in Prob. 2-24?

2-26. A water tank with an inside diameter of 6 ft and 10 ft long is to be butt-welded longitudinally. If water weighs 62.5 lb per cu ft, determine the commercial thickness of plate necessary to carry the load.

2-27. Compare the safe load carried by the riveted butt joint in Fig. 2-14 with the safe load carried by the same joint butt-welded together.

2-28. Two steel plates 10 in. wide are to be butt-welded together. Determine the commercial thickness necessary to carry a working tensile load of 65,000 lb.

3: Beams

3-1. Definition

A beam is a rigid body upon which are acting loads and reactions transverse to its axis. In buildings, bridges, and similar structures, beams are usually horizontal and the loads are weights. In machines, beams may have any direction and the loads may be pressures from other parts of the machine as well as weights. Loads on beams are either (1) concentrated loads, (2) uniformly distributed loads, or (3) a combination of both. A concentrated load is a single load acting at one point. A uniformly distributed load includes the weight of the beam and any load evenly distributed over it.

3-2. Kinds of Beams

Beams may be classified according to the type of support. A simple beam is one that rests on two supports, one at each end of the beam. Figure 3-1 shows a horizontal simple beam with two loads concentrated at two points, *A* and *B*. Figure 3-2 shows a horizontal simple beam with a uniformly distributed load of w lb per ft over its entire length l.

A single-overhang beam is one which overhangs one of its supports. Figure 3-3 shows a single-overhang beam with a

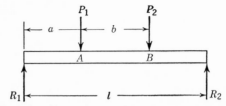

Fig. 3-1. Simple beam with concentrated loads.

Fig. 3-2. Simple beam with uniformly distributed load.

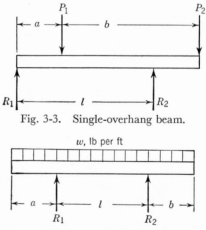

Fig. 3-3. Single-overhang beam.

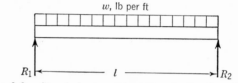

Fig. 3-4. Double-overhang beam.

concentrated load P_1 between the supports and another concentrated load P_2 overhanging.

A double-overhang beam is one which overhangs both of its supports. Figure 3-4 shows a double-overhang beam with a uniformly distributed load of w lb per ft over its entire length.

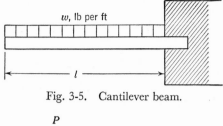

Fig. 3-5.   Cantilever beam.

Fig. 3-6.   Beam supported at one end and fixed at other end.

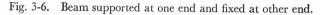

Fig. 3-7.   Beam fixed at both ends.

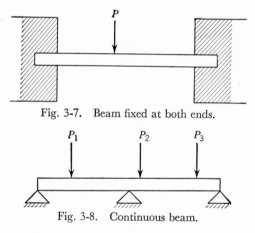

Fig. 3-8.   Continuous beam.

A cantilever beam is one fixed at one end and free at the other. Figure 3-5 shows a cantilever beam with a uniformly distributed load over its entire length l.

Other types of beams are (1) beam fixed at one end and supported at the other (Fig. 3-6), (2) beam fixed at both ends (Fig. 3-7), (3) continuous beam (Fig. 3-8).

Continuous beams will be discussed in a later chapter.

3-3. Reactions at Supports

The calculation of the reactions at the supports of a beam is a simple problem in Statics involving equilibrium of non-concurrent coplanar forces. In general, nonconcurrent coplanar force systems have three unknown quantities and require three independent equations, namely,

$$\Sigma F_x = 0 \qquad (3\text{-}1)$$

the algebraic sum of horizontal forces equals zero

$$\Sigma F_y = 0 \qquad (3\text{-}2)$$

the algebraic sum of vertical forces equals zero

$$\Sigma M = 0 \qquad (3\text{-}3)$$

the algebraic sum of the moments of the forces equals zero

When all the forces are vertical, as is the case with most beam problems, Eq. (3-1) is obviously useless.

Beams for which the reactions can be found from the equations of equilibrium are called *statically determinate* beams, and those for which the number of unknown reactions is greater than the number of equilibrium equations are called *statically indeterminate* beams. Simple beams, overhanging beams which rest on two supports, and cantilever beams are statically determinate; fixed and continuous beams are statically indeterminate and require additional equations for determining the reactions.

Statically determinate beam problems may be solved by two moment equations and then checked by a resolution equation, or by one moment and one resolution equation and checked by another moment equation. In either case, the amount of work is identical.

Example 3-1. Find the reactions at the supports of a uniform simple beam 12 ft long which weighs 60 lb per linear ft and carries a load of 1,200 lb at a point 4 ft from the left support.

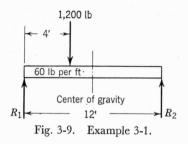

Fig. 3-9.   Example 3-1.

SOLUTION:

1. Since the beam is 12 ft long and weighs 60 lb per ft, the total weight is $(60)(12)$ lb. Since the center of gravity of a uniform beam is at the middle of its length, the moment arm of the uniform load is 6 ft from either support.

2. $$\Sigma M_{R_1} = 0$$
$$12R_2 - (1,200)4 - 60(12)(6) = 0$$
$$R_2 = 760 \text{ lb} \quad \text{ANS.}$$

3. $$\Sigma M_{R_2} = 0$$
$$12R_1 - (1,200)8 - 60(12)(6) = 0$$
$$R_1 = 1,160 \text{ lb} \quad \text{ANS.}$$

4. *Check:* $$\Sigma F_y = 0$$
$$760 + 1,160 = 1,200 + 720$$
$$1,920 = 1,920$$

Example 3-2.   Calculate the reactions at the supports of the beam as shown in Fig. 3-10.

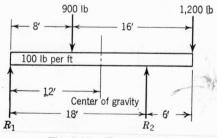

Fig. 3-10.   Example 3-2.

76   *Beams*

SOLUTION: Reactions are found as in the previous example.

1. $\Sigma M_{R_1} = 0$

$-18R_2 + (900)8 + (1,200)24 + (100)(24)(12) = 0$

$$18R_2 = 64,800$$
$$R_2 = 3,600 \text{ lb}$$

2. $\Sigma M_{R_2} = 0$

$18R_1 - (900)10 - (100)(24)6 + (1,200)6 = 0$

$$18R_1 = 16,200$$
$$R_1 = 900 \text{ lb}$$

3. *Check:* $\Sigma F_y = 0$

$$900 + 3,600 = 900 + 1,200 + 2,400$$
$$4,500 = 4,500$$

PROBLEMS

3-1. Calculate the reactions at the supports of a uniform simple beam with a uniform load of 120 lb per ft over the entire length of 24 ft and concentrated loads of 2,000 and 1,800 lb located 5 and 14 ft, respectively, from the left end.   Check the results.

3-2. Find the reactions and check the following problem (Fig. 3-11).

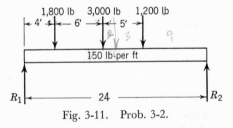

Fig. 3-11.   Prob. 3-2.

3-3. A beam 20 ft long weighing 90 lb per ft is supported at both ends and carries a load of 1,500 lb at a point 12 ft from the left support.   Find the reactions and check.

In the following problems, find the reactions and check.

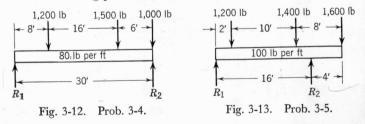

Fig. 3-12.   Prob. 3-4.   Fig. 3-13.   Prob. 3-5.

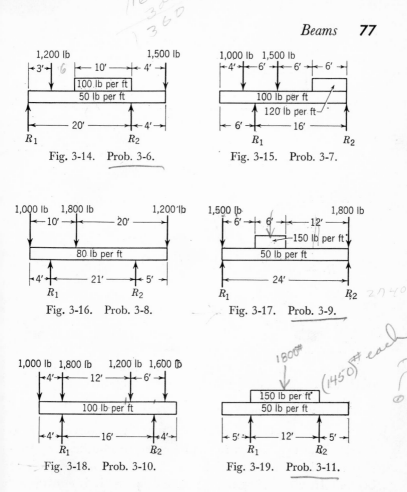

Fig. 3-14. Prob. 3-6.

Fig. 3-15. Prob. 3-7.

Fig. 3-16. Prob. 3-8.

Fig. 3-17. Prob. 3-9.

Fig. 3-18. Prob. 3-10.

Fig. 3-19. Prob. 3-11.

3-4. Cantilever Beam

Since this is a beam which is fixed at one end, with no support at the other, the only reaction that can occur is at the fixed end (see Fig. 3-20). The reaction consists of an upward pressure R_1 on the part of the beam just within the wall and a downward pressure R_2 on the end of the beam. If we assume R_1 to act at a distance a from the face of the wall and R_2 to act at a distance b from the same face, then by $\Sigma M = 0$

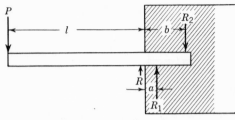

Fig. 3-20.   Cantilever beam.

about the points of application of R_1 and R_2, we get

$$R_1 = \frac{P(l + b)}{b - a} \quad \text{and} \quad R_2 = \frac{P(l + a)}{b - a}$$

$$R_1 - R_2 = \frac{P(l + b)}{b - a} - \frac{P(l + a)}{b - a}$$

or

$$R_1 - R_2 = P$$

as it should.

Consequently, the reaction R at the wall is simply the sum of all the loads on the beam and oppositely directed.

3-5.   Vertical Shear and Bending Moment

When a beam is loaded, the loads and reactions cause it to bend.   The bending is resisted by certain tensile, compressive, and shear stresses which are set up in the material of the beam.   In visualizing these internal forces, it is convenient to consider the beam to be composed of an infinite number of fibers extending the length of the beam.   The fibers in the upper portion will be shortened, and therefore will be in compression; the fibers in the lower portion will be lengthened and therefore will be in tension.   Somewhere between the top and bottom of the beam there is a plane where the length of the fibers remains unchanged by the bending of the beam.   This plane is known as the *neutral plane* or *axis*.

If the beam in Fig. 3-21 is cut through any section *A–A*, and the portion of the beam to the right of the section is removed, forces equivalent to those which the right portion exerted on the left portion must be applied on section *A–A* in order

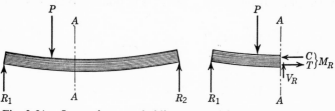

Fig. 3-21.   Internal stresses holding external forces in equilibrium.

to hold that portion of the beam in equilibrium, since it was in equilibrium before the beam was cut.

To prevent rotation about R_1, there must be a vertical force V_R acting in an upward direction at section *A–A*.   This vertical force is a vertical-shear resisting force equal in magnitude to the resultant of the external forces (loads and reactions) that lie on the one side of the section.   If *P* is a concen-

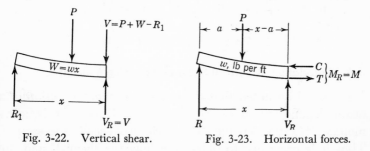

Fig. 3-22.   Vertical shear.   Fig. 3-23.   Horizontal forces.

trated load, *W* is the total distributed load, R_1 is the reaction at the left end of the beam, and *V* is the resultant vertical shear at section *A–A* (Fig. 3-22), then $V = P + W - R_1$ and $V_R = V$.

To resist bending there must be a horizontal couple M_R composed of a compressive force *C* on the upper fibers and a tensile force T on the lower fibers (Fig. 3-23). This horizontal couple is a resisting moment equal in magnitude to the resultant, or algebraic sum, of the bending moments, about the section, of the external forces that lie on the one side of the section. If bending moment is denoted by the symbol M,

$$M = R_1x - P(x - a) - wx\left(\frac{x}{2}\right)$$

or

$$M = R_1x - P(x - a) - \frac{wx^2}{2} \tag{3-4}$$

Since the bending moment is equal to the resisting moment, $M = M_R$.

Since the only horizontal forces are the compressive stress C and the tensile stress T, for equilibrium, $C = T$.

To summarize, since any portion of the beam (Figs. 3-21–3-23 is in equilibrium, the forces acting on the portion must satisfy the equations of equilibrium:

$$\Sigma F_x = 0 \quad \text{or} \quad C = T$$
$$\Sigma F_y = 0 \quad \text{or} \quad V = V_R$$
$$\Sigma M = 0 \quad \text{or} \quad M = M_R$$

3-6. Calculation of Vertical Shear and Bending Moment

It should be noted that the stress at any cross section of a beam depends upon the shearing force V and the bending moment M, and that the stress varies from section to section. Thus it is necessary to determine how the shear V and the moment M vary from section to section. For such purpose it is necessary to adopt and use certain rules of signs for V and M.

It is customary to regard upward acting forces as positive, downward acting forces as negative. V being the resultant of vertical forces acting at any section, it will be positive or negative according to whether the algebraic sum of all forces to the left of the section is positive or negative.

M is regarded as positive or negative according as the moment of all forces to the left of the section, about a moment center or pivot in the section, is clockwise or counterclockwise.

3-7. Notation

V_x and M_x, respectively, denote shearing force and bending moment at a section x distant from a stated origin or zero point. Likewise, V_4 and M_4 denote shearing force and bending moment at a section 4 ft from the zero point. It is customary to solve problems by using the left end of the beam as the starting point, although they may be worked equally well by using the right end as the starting point.

A positive bending moment denotes a downward bending of the beam, indicating that the upper fibers are in compression and the lower fibers in tension. A negative bending moment

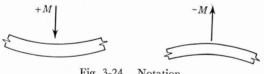

Fig. 3-24.   Notation.

denotes an upward bending of the beam, indicating that the upper fibers are in tension and the lower fibers in compression (Fig. 3-24).

Example 3-3.   Calculate the shearing force V and the bending moment M for various cross sections of the beam described in Fig. 3-9, observing the rules of signs stated above.

SOLUTION:

1. R_1 and R_2 are 1,160 and 760 lb, respectively, as previously calculated.

2. Vertical shear: $\qquad V_x = R_1 - P - W_x$

At R_1: $\qquad\qquad\qquad V_{R_1} = 0$

To the right at R_1: $V_{R_1} = 1,160$ lb

To the left of 4 ft: $\quad V_4 = 1,160 - (60)(4) = 920$ lb

To the right of 4 ft: $V_4 = 1,160 - (60)(4) - 1,200$
$$= -280 \text{ lb}$$

At 8 ft: $\qquad\qquad\qquad V_8 = 1,160 - (60)(8) - 1,200$
$$= -520 \text{ lb}$$

To the left of R_2: $\quad V_{R_2} = 1,160 - (60)(12) - 1,200$
$$= -760 \text{ lb}$$

At R_2: $\qquad\qquad\qquad V_{R_2} = 1,160 - (60)(12) - 1,200 + \overset{\scriptsize{---}}{1,200}$
$$= 0$$

Inspection of the results obtained will indicate that the magnitude of vertical shear at any point is equal to the algebraic sum of the loads between that point and the previously calculated point. This leads to a shorter method of calculation as follows:

At R_1: $\qquad\qquad\qquad V_{R_1} = 0$

To the right of R_1: $V_{R_1} = +1,160$
$$\underline{\phantom{V_{R_1} = }- \quad 240}$$

To the left of 4 ft: $\quad V_4 = \qquad 920$
$$\underline{-1,200}$$

To the right of 4 ft: $V_4 = - \quad 280$
$$\underline{- \quad 240}$$

At 8 ft: $\qquad\qquad\qquad V_8 = - \quad 520$
$$\underline{- \quad 240}$$

To the left of R_2: $\quad V_{R_2} = - \quad 760$
$$\underline{\phantom{V_{R_2} = }+ \quad 760}$$

At R_2: $\qquad\qquad\qquad V_{R_2} = \qquad\quad 0$

3. Bending moments:

$$M_x = R_1 x - P(x - a) - \frac{wx^2}{2}$$

$M_{R_1} = 0$

$M_2 = 1,160 \times 2 \quad - (60 \times 2 \times 1) \quad = 2,200$ lb-ft

$M_4 = 1,160 \times 4 \quad - (60 \times 4 \times 2) \quad - 1,200 \times 0 = 4,160$ lb-ft

$M_6 = 1,160 \times 6 \quad - (60 \times 6 \times 3) \quad - 1,200 \times 2 = 3,480$ lb-ft

$M_8 = 1,160 \times 8 \quad - (60 \times 8 \times 4) \quad - 1,200 \times 4 = 2,560$ lb-ft

$M_{10} = 1,160 \times 10 - (60 \times 10 \times 5) - 1,200 \times 6 = 1,400$ lb-ft

$M_{12} = 1,160 \times 12 - (60 \times 12 \times 6) - 1,200 \times 8 = 0$

3-8. Vertical-shear and Bending-moment Diagrams

A graphical representation, or diagram, will convey correlated data more rapidly than a tabulated description, because diagrams are more easily understood and require less mental effort than would be necessary to determine the facts from complex tables.

A vertical-shear diagram is a graphical representation of the variation of the vertical-shear resisting forces along the full length of a beam.

A bending-moment diagram is a graphical representation of the variation of the bending moments along the full length of the beam.

Vertical-shear and bending-moment diagrams show at a glance how the shearing force V and the bending moment M vary from section to section. They also show the relations among vertical shear, bending moment, and external forces. Every properly worked design of a beam should include its corresponding shear and moment diagrams.

3-9. Construction of Shear and Moment Diagrams

The loaded beam is first drawn to some convenient scale. The shear and moment diagrams are then drawn directly below the loaded beam, to the same horizontal scale. The abscissas of successive points on all three diagrams thus represent the same locations of successive cross sections of the beam. The ordinate of each point on the shear diagram will represent the vertical shear at that particular cross section, while the ordinate on the moment diagram will represent the bending moment.

To illustrate the construction of shear and moment diagrams, three examples will be considered: (1) a beam with a concentrated load, (2) a beam with a uniformly distributed load, and (3) a beam with both types of load.

Example 3-4. Draw the vertical-shear and bending-moment diagrams for a beam 10 ft long which carries a load of 5,000 lb at its mid-point.

SOLUTION:

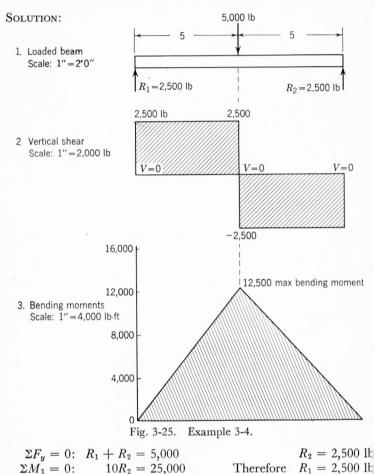

1. Loaded beam
   Scale: $1'' = 2'0''$

2. Vertical shear
   Scale: $1'' = 2,000$ lb

3. Bending moments
   Scale: $1'' = 4,000$ lb·ft

Fig. 3-25.   Example 3-4.

$$\Sigma F_y = 0: \quad R_1 + R_2 = 5,000 \qquad\qquad R_2 = 2,500 \text{ lb}$$
$$\Sigma M_1 = 0: \quad 10R_2 = 25,000 \qquad \text{Therefore} \quad R_1 = 2,500 \text{ lb}$$

Vertical shear:

At R_1:	$V_{R_1} =$	0
To the right of R_1:	$V_{R_1} =$	2,500
To the left of 5 ft:	$V_5 =$	2,500
		$-5,000$
To the right of 5 ft:	$V_5 =$	$-2,500$
To the left of R_2:	$V_{R_2} =$	$-2,500$
		$+2,500$
At R_2:	$V_{R_2} =$	0

Bending moments:

$$M_{R_1} = 0$$
$$M_2 = (2,500)2 = 5,000 \text{ lb-ft}$$
$$M_5 = (2,500)5 = 12,500 \text{ lb-ft}$$
$$M_6 = (2,500)6 - (5,000)1 = 10,000 \text{ lb-ft}$$
$$M_8 = (2,500)8 - (5,000)3 = 5,000 \text{ lb-ft}$$
$$M_{10} = (2,500)10 - (5,000)5 = 0$$

Example 3-5.   Draw the shear and moment diagrams for a beam 10 ft long which carries a uniformly distributed load of 500 lb per ft of length.

SOLUTION: See Fig. 3-26.

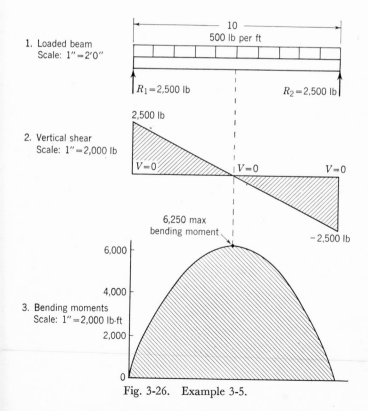

Fig. 3-26.   Example 3-5.

86   *Beams*

Example 3-6. Draw the vertical-shear and bending-moment diagrams for the data of Example 3-3.

SOLUTION: See Fig. 3-27.

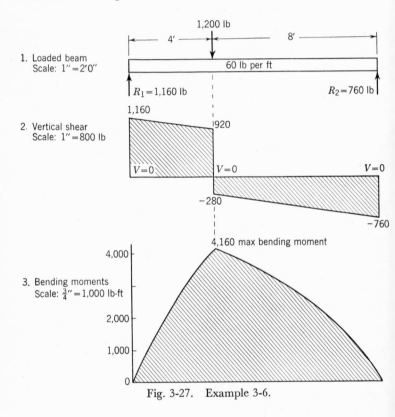

Fig. 3-27.   Example 3-6.

3-10. Observations from Shear and Moment Diagrams

Inspection of the shear and moment diagrams in Figs. 3-25, 3-26, and 3-27 illustrates the following relations among loads, shears, and bending moments:

1. For any part of the beam where there is no loading, the shear line is a horizontal line, and the moment line is a diagonal line.

2. For any part of the beam where there is a uniformly distributed load, the shear line is a diagonal line sloping downward to the right and the moment line is a parabolic curve, concave downward.

3. For a beam with both concentrated and uniformly distributed loads, the shear line is a diagonal line sloping downward to the right, except at the point or points of concentrated loading. At these points, it is a vertical line. The moment line is similar to a parabolic curve, but irregularly shaped (nonsymmetric).

4. The maximum shearing forces occur at sections adjacent to supports. Hence, to determine the largest shearing force, calculate the value of V for each side of each support, and note which is the largest (numerically).

5. The section of maximum bending moment (the danger section), is not quite so obvious. Inspection of both shear and moment diagrams will show that a section of maximum bending moment is also a section where the shearing force $V = 0$. Therefore, to determine where M is a maximum, calculate the section or sections of zero shear $(V = 0)$, calculate M for each such section, and compare for the largest value. A positive or negative result merely indicates downward or upward bending of the beam (see Art. 3-7).

3-11. Procedure for Solution of Beam Problems

The following procedure should be followed for constructing shear and bending-moment diagrams:

1. Calculate the reactions at the supports by the principle of moments and then check by summation of vertical forces.

2. Calculate vertical shear for all critical points and determine points of zero shear.

3. Calculate bending moments for all critical points. Maximum bending moment will be at point of zero shear.

4. Draw the shear and moment diagrams to some convenient scale, directly below a space diagram of the beam.

Example 3-7. Construct the shear and bending-moment diagrams, locate the point of zero shear, and determine the maximum bending moment for the beam in Fig. 3-28.

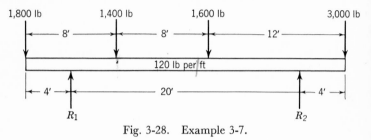

Fig. 3-28. Example 3-7.

SOLUTION: We calculate the reactions at the supports.

$$\Sigma M_{R_2} = 0$$
$$20R_1 + (3,000)4 = (1,800)24 + (1,400)16 + (1,600)8$$
$$+ (120)(28)10$$
$$R_1 = 5,000 \text{ lb}$$
$$\Sigma M_{R_1} = 0$$
$$20R_2 + (1,800)4 = (1,400)4 + (1,600)12 + (3,000)24$$
$$+ (120)(28)10$$
$$R_2 = 6,160 \text{ lb}$$

Check:
$$\Sigma F_y = 0$$
$$5,000 + 6,160 = 1,800 + 1,400 + 1,600 + 3,000 + 3,360$$
$$11,160 = 11,160$$

Next we calculate values for vertical shear, using the short method of calculation:

To the left of the load: $V_0 = 0$
$$-1,800$$
To the right of the load: $V_0 = -1,800$
$$-480$$
To the left of R_1: $V_{R_1} = -2,280$
$$+5,000$$
To the right of R_1: $V_{R_1} = +2,720$
$$-480$$
To the left of 8 ft: $V_8 = +2,240$
$$-1,400$$

To the right of 8 ft:	$V_8 =$	840
		$- 960$
To the left of 16 ft:	$V_{16} = $	$- 120$
		$-1{,}600$
To the right of 16 ft:	$V_{16} = $	$-1{,}720$
		$- 960$
To the left of R_2:	$V_{R_2} = $	$-2{,}680$
		$+6{,}160$
To the right of R_2:	$V_{R_2} = $	$+3{,}480$
		$- 480$
To the left of 28 ft:	$V_{28} = $	$+3{,}000$
		$-3{,}000$
At 28 ft:	$V_{28} = $	0

Two points of zero shear are the two ends of the beam. Other points are where vertical shear changes sign. Two such points are at the supports R_1 and R_2. A fifth point is between 8 and 16 ft, since $V_8 = +820$ lb and $V_{16} = -120$ lb. Since $V_8 = 840$ and vertical shear between 8 and 16 ft keeps dropping at the rate of 120 lb per ft, vertical shear will be zero at a point $X = {}^{840}\!/_{120} = 7$ ft to the right of 8 ft.

Therefore points of zero shear are 0, 4, 15, 24, and 30 ft.

Next we calculate bending moments for all critical points.

$$M_0 = 0$$
$$M_{R_1} = -(1{,}800)(4) - (120)(4)(2) = -8160 \text{ lb-ft}$$
$$M_8 = -(1{,}800)(8) - (120)(8)(4) + (5{,}000)(4) = 1{,}760 \text{ lb-ft}$$
$$M_{15} = (1{,}800)(15) - (1{,}400)(7) - (120)(15)(7.5) + (5{,}000)(11)$$
$$= 4{,}700 \text{ lb-ft}$$
$$M_{16} = -(1{,}800)(16) - (1{,}400)(8) - (120)(16)(8) + (5{,}000)(12)$$
$$= 4{,}640 \text{ lb-ft}$$
$$M_{R_2} = -(1{,}800)(24) - (1{,}400)(16) - (1{,}600)(8)$$
$$- (120)(24)(12) + (5{,}000)(20) = -12{,}960 \text{ lb-ft}$$
$$M_{28} = -(1{,}800)(28) - (1{,}400)(20) - (1{,}600)(12)$$
$$- (120)(28)(14) + (5{,}000)(24) + (6{,}160)(4) = 0$$

Maximum positive bending moment: $M_{15} = 4{,}700$ lb-ft
Maximum negative bending moment: $M_{R_2} = -12{,}960$ lb-ft
We now plot the shear and moment diagrams.

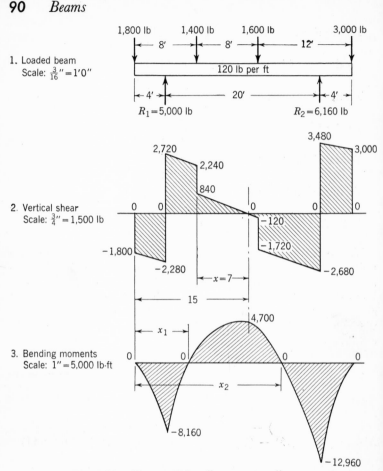

Fig. 3-29.   Shear and bending-moment diagram.

PROBLEMS

3-12–3-19. Construct the shear and moment diagrams, locating the points of zero shear and determining the maximum bending moments for Probs. 3-4–3-11, Figs. 3-12–3-19, inclusive.

3-12. Shear and Moment Diagrams for Cantilever Beams

In the solution of the cantilever beam, the only reaction R at the fixed end (Art. 3-4) is equal to the total load on the beam and oppositely directed. If upward forces are considered positive and downward forces negative, vertical shear at any section of a cantilever beam is the algebraic sum of the forces acting from the section to the free end. Similarly, the bending moments are calculated by considering the forces between the section and the free end.

Example 3-8. Plot the shear and bending-moment diagrams for the following beam.

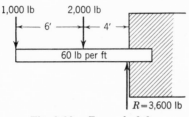

Fig. 3-30. Example 3-8.

SOLUTION: $R = 1,000 + 2,000 + 60 \times 10$
$R = 3,600$ lb

Vertical shear:

To the left of the load: $V_0 = 0$
$-1,000$
To the right of the load: $V_0 = -1,000$
-360
To the left of 6 ft: $V_6 = -1,360$
$-2,000$
To the right of 6 ft: $V_6 = -3,360$
-240
To the left of R: $V_R = -3,600$
$+3,600$
To the right of R: $V_R = 0$

The points of zero shear are the two ends of the beam.

Bending moments:

$$M_0 = 0$$
$$M_3 = -(1,000)(3) - (60)(3)(1.5) = -3,270 \text{ lb-ft}$$
$$M_6 = -(1,000)(6) - (60)(6)(3) = -7,080 \text{ lb-ft}$$
$$M_R = -(1,000)(10) - (60 \times 10)(5) = -13,000 \text{ lb-ft}$$

Maximum bending moment, therefore, occurs at the support (Fig. 3-31).

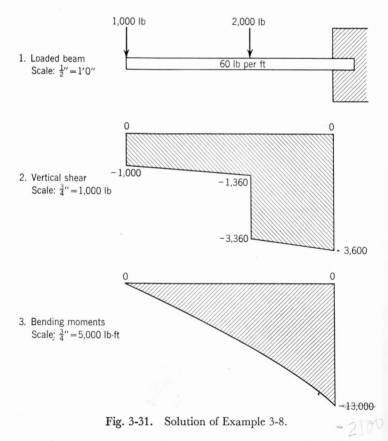

Fig. 3-31. Solution of Example 3-8.

PROBLEMS

3-20. A cantilever beam 10 ft long is fixed at the right end and carries a load of 2,000 lb at the left end and a uniformly distributed load of 50 lb per ft.   Draw the vertical-shear and bending-moment diagrams.

3-21. A cantilever beam 12 ft long and fixed at the left end carries a load of 2,400 lb at the right end and a load of 3,000 lb at a point 8 ft from the fixed end.   Neglecting the weight of the beam, plot the shear and moment diagrams.

3-22. A cantilever beam fixed at the right end weighs 80 lb per linear ft and is 12 ft long.   It carries a load of 1,200 lb at the right end and a uniformly distributed load of 60 lb per ft from the fixed end to its mid-point.   Plot the shear and moment diagrams.

3-23. Draw the vertical-shear and bending-moment diagrams for Fig. 3-32.

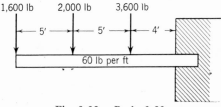

Fig. 3-32.   Prob. 3-23.

3-24. Draw the vertical-shear and bending-moment diagrams for Fig. 3-33.

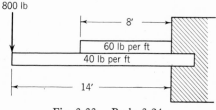

Fig. 3-33.   Prob. 3-24.

3-13.   Derivation of the General Bending-moment Equation

Figure 3-34*a* represents a simple beam with a concentrated load P and a load w uniformly distributed over its entire length. Let this beam be cut along two sections $A–A$ and $B–B$ that are x ft apart. Let M_1 and M_2 be the bending

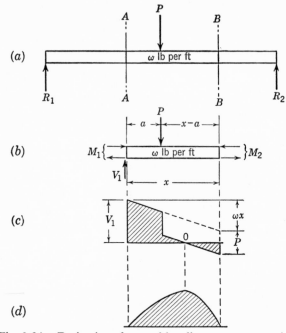

Fig. 3-34.   Derivation of general bending-moment equation.

moments of sections $A–A$ and $B–B$, respectively, V_1 be the vertical shear at section $A–A$, and let P act at a distance a feet from section $A–A$. Since the full beam is in equilibrium, any part of it likewise is in equilibrium. Therefore we have

$$\Sigma M = 0$$

$$M_1 + V_1 x - P(x - a) - wx \times \frac{x}{2} - M_2 = 0$$

which may be written

$$M_2 = M_1 + V_1 x - P(x - a) - \frac{wx^2}{2} \qquad (3\text{-}5)$$

This is the equation for the bending moment at section *B–B* of the cut segment. It also applies to any segment of any beam and is therefore called the *general bending-moment equation*. Comparison of Eq. (3-5) with Eq. (3-4) will show that they become identical when section *A–A* is taken to be the left end of the beam.

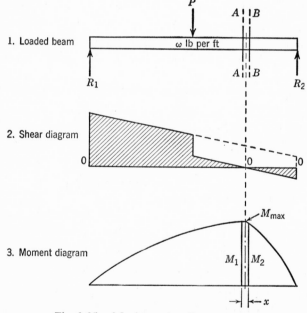

Fig. 3-35. Maximum bending moment.

Now, in the same beam (Fig. 3-35) let section *A–A* be taken just to the left of the maximum bending moment M_{max} and section *B–B* just to the right of it. As the distance *x* between the section is decreased, M_1 and M_2 will approach each other in magnitude as they approach M_{max}. As this occurs, the value of vertical shear also reduces toward zero. The point at which M_1 equals M_2 is the maximum moment point where $M_1 = M_2 = M_{max}$. This point is attained only when vertical shear is equal to zero. Therefore a maximum bending moment is obtained whenever vertical shear equals zero (when the shear diagram cuts the horizontal axis).

3-14. Points of Inflection

A beam which overhangs one or both of its supports may bend concave downward throughout part of its length and concave upward throughout the rest of its length, as shown in Fig. 3-29. Such a beam may have negative as well as positive bending moments. Since the moment must change from a negative to a positive value (or vice versa), it must be zero at some in-between section. The section in a beam at which the bending moment is zero is called the *point of inflection*. A single overhanging beam will have one point of inflection; a double overhanging beam will have two such points (Fig. 3-36).

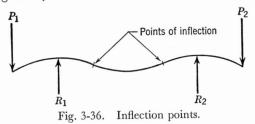

Fig. 3-36. Inflection points.

To locate a point of inflection in a beam, we merely set up an expression for bending moment and set it equal to zero.

Example 3-9. Calculate the points of inflection for the beam of Fig. 3-29.

SOLUTION: The bending moment x_1 ft from the left end of the beam is

$$M_{x_1} = -1{,}800x_1 + 5{,}000(x_1 - 4) - 120x_1 \frac{x_1}{2}$$

Equating to zero, rearranging, and simplifying, we have

$$3x_1{}^2 - 160x_1 + 1{,}000 = 0$$

By use of the quadratic formula, we obtain

$$x_1 = \frac{-b \pm \sqrt{b^2 - 4ac}}{2a} = \frac{160 \pm \sqrt{25{,}600 - 4(3)(1{,}000)}}{6}$$

$$x_1 = \frac{160 \pm 117}{6}$$

$$x_1 = \frac{160 - 117}{6} = \frac{43}{6} = 7.2 \text{ ft}$$

$$x_1 = \frac{160 + 117}{6} = \frac{277}{6} = 46.2 \text{ ft}$$

It should be evident that 7.2 ft is the correct answer, since it is within the limits of the curve on the moment diagram. The 46.2-ft answer is the second solution to the quadratic equation, but obviously has no meaning for this problem.

The bending moment which is x_2 ft from the left end of the beam is

$$M_{x_2} = -1{,}800x_2 + 5{,}000(x_2 - 4)$$
$$- 1{,}400(x_2 - 8) - 1{,}600(x_2 - 16) - \frac{120x_2{}^2}{2}$$

As before

$$3x_2{}^2 - 10x_2 - 840 = 0$$

$$x_2 = \frac{10 \pm \sqrt{10{,}180}}{6} = \frac{10 \pm 101}{6}$$

$$x_2 = \frac{111}{6} = 18.5 \text{ ft}$$

PROBLEMS

3-25–3-31. Calculate the inflection points for Prob. 3-5, Fig. 3-13, through Prob. 3-11, Fig. 3-19, inclusive.

3-32–3-36. For the shear diagrams of Figs. 3-37–3-41, make

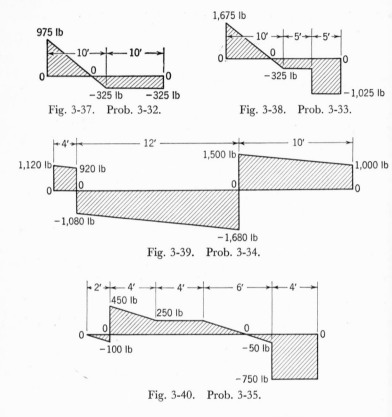

975 lb

10' → 10'

0

0

−325 lb   −325 lb

Fig. 3-37. Prob. 3-32.

1,675 lb

10' → 5' → 5'

0   0   0

−325 lb

−1,025 lb

Fig. 3-38. Prob. 3-33.

4' → 12' → 10'

1,500 lb

1,120 lb   920 lb   1,000 lb

0   0   0

−1,080 lb

−1,680 lb

Fig. 3-39. Prob. 3-34.

2' → 4' → 4' → 6' → 4'

450 lb

250 lb

0   0   0

−100 lb   −50 lb

−750 lb

Fig. 3-40. Prob. 3-35.

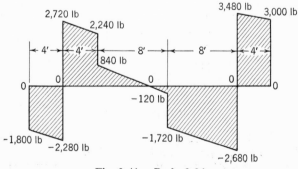

2,720 lb

2,240 lb

3,480 lb   3,000 lb

4' → 4' → 8' → 8' → 4'

840 lb

0   0   0   0

−120 lb

−1,800 lb   −2,280 lb   −1,720 lb

−2,680 lb

Fig. 3-41. Prob. 3-36.

sketches of the beams with loads in their correct positions. Also draw the bending-moment diagrams.

3-15. Construction of Moment Diagrams by Shear-area Method

Equation (3-5) for calculating the bending moment of any section may be written

$$M_2 - M_1 = V_1 x - P(x - a) - \frac{wx^2}{2} \qquad (3\text{-}6)$$

The left side of this equation is the difference, or change, in bending moment between any two vertical sections of a beam. The right side of this equation is the net area under the shear diagram between the same two vertical sections of the beam, namely, the rectangle $V_1 x$ minus the parallelogram $P(x - a)$ and the triangle $wx^2/2$ (see Fig. 3-34).

Stated more simply, Equation (3-6) says that the change in bending moment between any two points along the length of a beam is equal to the area of the shear diagram between the same two points.

This principle can be used advantageously to construct bending-moment diagrams. As before, the loaded beam is drawn to some convenient scale, the reactions are calculated, and the shear diagram is drawn directly below the loaded beam. Bending moments at pertinent points along the beam are then calculated by cumulatively totaling the areas of the shear diagram, from left to right.

For our illustration, let us return to the beam of Example 3-6, Fig. 3-29.

Example 3-10. Construct the bending-moment diagram for Example 3-6, Fig. 3-29 by the shear-area method.

SOLUTION: The loaded beam and vertical-shear diagram are constructed as before (Fig. 3-42).

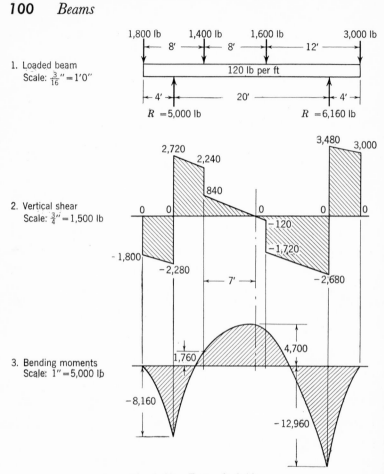

1. Loaded beam
   Scale: $\frac{3}{16}'' = 1'0''$

2. Vertical shear
   Scale: $\frac{3}{4}'' = 1,500$ lb

3. Bending moments
   Scale: $1'' = 5,000$ lb

Fig. 3-42.   Example 3-10.

We now calculate bending moments for the significant points, which are at the concentrated loads and the reactions.

$$M_4 = -1,800 \times 4 - 480 \times 4 \times \tfrac{1}{2} = -8,160$$
$$+2,240 \times 4 + 480 \times 4 \times \tfrac{1}{2} = +9,920$$
$$M_8 = +1,760$$
$$+840 \times 7 \times \tfrac{1}{2} = +2,940$$

$$M_{15} = + 4,700$$
$$-120 \times 1 \times \tfrac{1}{2} = - 60$$
$$M_{16} = + 4,640$$
$$-1,720 \times 8 - 960 \times 8 \times \tfrac{1}{2} = -17,600$$
$$M_{24} = -12,960$$
$$+3,000 \times 4 + 480 \times 4 \times \tfrac{1}{2} = +12,960$$
$$M_{28} = 0$$

Since each bending-moment value was based on the preceding one, and the moment at the right end of the beam equals zero, we have a check on the intermediate computations, and the problem is complete. Should the moment at the right end of the beam not equal zero, the computations are in error and must be corrected.

It should be noted that in order to follow the convention regarding the algebraic signs of shears and bending moments, the shear areas must be summed up from left to right. If the bending-moment diagram is started at the right end and worked toward the left, the sign of each shear area must be reversed.

PROBLEMS

3-37–3-43. Construct the bending-moment diagrams for Probs. 3-5–3-11, Figs. 3-13–3-19, inclusive, by the shear-area method.

3-16. Maximum Shear and Bending Moment Due to Moving Loads

Heretofore, in calculating shear and bending moment, it was assumed that the loads on the beam were fixed, or static, loads. However, this is not always the case. An auto or

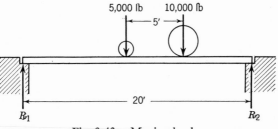

Fig. 3-43. Moving loads.

other vehicle passing over a bridge, a piece of furniture or equipment being moved over a floor are examples of systems of moving concentrated loads which are at fixed distances from each other.

In computing vertical shear for simple beams acted upon by concentrated loads, or uniformly distributed loads, or both, it was noted that the maximum shear always occurred at one of the reactions. Moreover, the maximum shear was equal to the maximum reaction. For a system of moving loads, the maximum shear will also occur at one of the reactions, and it will also equal its maximum reaction. Therefore, in order to determine the maximum shear due to a system of rolling loads, we merely locate the loads to create a maximum reaction. Care must be taken not to change their position with respect to each other.

Example 3-11. Determine the maximum vertical shear that can be produced on the beam of Fig. 3-43.

SOLUTION: In Fig. 3-44, if the loads were in position 1, the reaction R_1 would be

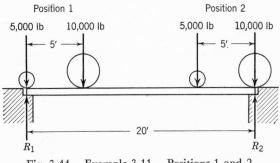

Fig. 3-44. Example 3-11. Positions 1 and 2.

$$R_1 = 5,000 + {}^{15}\!/_{20}(10,000) = 5,000 + 7,500 = 12,500 \text{ lb}$$

If the loads were placed in position 2, the reaction R_2 would be

$$R_2 = 10,000 + {}^{15}\!/_{20}(5,000) = 10,000 + 3,750 = 13,750 \text{ lb}$$

If the loads were placed in position 3 (Fig. 3-45), the reaction R_1 would be

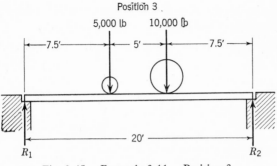

Fig. 3-45. Example 3-11. Position 3.

$$R_1 = \frac{12.5}{20} (5,000) + \frac{7.5}{20} (10,000) = 6,875 \text{ lb}$$

The reaction R_2 would be

$$R_2 = \frac{7.5}{20} (5,000) + \frac{12.5}{20} (10,000) = 8,125 \text{ lb}$$

Comparison of the magnitudes of the reactions for the three positions considered indicate that the closer the heavier loads can be placed near a reaction, the greater will be its magnitude. The maximum shear in this problem is 13,750 lb of position 2.

Maximum Bending Moment. In a system of rolling loads, the bending moment under any one of the loads will not necessarily be the same as that under another of the loads; nor will the moment be constant under the loads as they move from one end of the beam to the other. When the loads are in any given position on the beam, the maximum moment must occur under one of the loads, since the vertical shear must pass through zero under one of them. Therefore, the problem is to find the maximum bending moment under each load separately. The greatest of these moments is the *maximum* bending moment to which the beam is subjected, and the one used in its design.

In Fig. 3-46, let P be the resultant of concentrated loads p_1,

p_2, p_3, and p_4; d_1, d_2, and d_3 be fixed distances between them on a simple beam of length l.   Let e be the distance from any one of the loads, say, p_2, to the resultant load P, and X be the required distance between the load p_2 and reaction R_1 which will give a maximum bending moment.   With the assistance

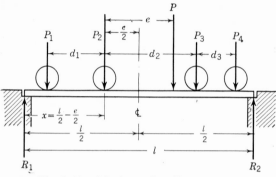

Fig. 3-46.   Maximum bending moment.

of some more advanced mathematics, it is proved that

$$X = \frac{1}{2} - \frac{e}{2}$$

This equation may be stated as follows: Any load will be in its position of maximum bending moment when that load is as far on one side of the center of the beam as the resultant of all the loads on the beam is on the other side of the center.

To find the *greatest* maximum bending moment to which the beam is subjected, each load must be placed in its position of maximum moment, and the bending moment at this point must be found.   The one which is numerically greatest is then selected as the solution to the problem.

Example 3-12.   Compute the maximum bending moment for the truck-trailer combination of Fig. 3-47 as it travels across the simply supported span of 50 ft.

SOLUTION: The resultant of the three loads is

$$P = 2,000 + 4,000 + 4,000 = 10,000 \text{ lb}$$

The location of P with respect to the three loads is found by

$$10,000X = (4,000)20 + (2,000)30$$
$$X = 14 \text{ ft} \quad \text{from load } C$$

The position of the load system to give a maximum bending moment under A is shown in Fig. 3-47a in accordance with the rule

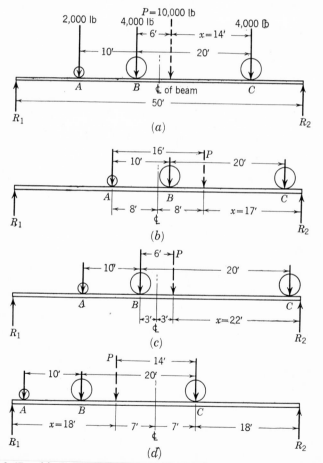

Fig. 3-47. (*a*) Original loading. (*b*) Maximum moment at *A*. (*c*) Maximum moment at *B*. (*d*) Maximum moment at *C*.

that the center line of the beam be midway between A and P. Taking moments about R_2 equal to zero,

$$50R_1 = (10,000)17 \qquad (\Sigma M_{R_2} = 0)$$
$$R_1 = 3,400 \text{ lb}$$

and bending moment at A is

$$M_A = (3,400)17 = 57,800 \text{ lb-ft}$$

The position of the load system to give a maximum bending moment at B next requires that the mid-point of the beam be placed midway between B and P (Fig. 3-47b).   Again

$$50R_1 = (10,000)22 \qquad (\Sigma M_{R_2} = 0)$$
$$R_1 = 4,400 \text{ lb}$$

and bending moment at B is

$$M_B = (4,400)22 - (2,000)10 = 76,800 \text{ lb-ft}$$

Finally, the position of the load system to give a maximum bending moment at C requires that the center of the beam be placed midway between C and P (Fig. 3-47c).   Again

$$50R_2 = (10,000)18 \qquad (\Sigma M_{R_1} = 0)$$
$$R_2 = 3,600 \text{ lb}$$

and bending moment at C is

$$M_C = (3,600)18 = 64,000 \text{ lb-ft}$$

A comparison of the above results shows that the most dangerous bending moment is 76,800 lb-ft, which occurs under load B.

PROBLEMS

3-44. A truck with axle loads of 4,000 and 6,000 lb on a wheel base of 12 ft, as shown in Fig. 3-48, rolls across a 30-ft span.   Compute maximum bending moment and maximum shearing force.

3-45. Repeat Prob. 3-44 for axle loads of 8,000 and 12,000 lb on a wheel base of 14 ft (Fig. 3-49) rolling across a 40-ft span.

3-46. Determine the position of the axle loads shown in Fig. 3-50 to produce a maximum bending moment and shear on a 30-ft span.

3-47. Repeat Prob. 3-46 for a span of 20 ft.

28000

3-48. Determine the position of the axle loads shown in Fig. 3-51 to produce a maximum bending moment and shear for a 40-ft span.

3-49. Repeat Prob. 3-48 for a span of 50 ft.

3-50. A truck-trailer combination crossing a 40-ft span has axle loads of 4,000, 8,000, and 12,000 lb, separated by distances as shown in Fig. 3-52. Compute the maximum bending moment and shear force developed.

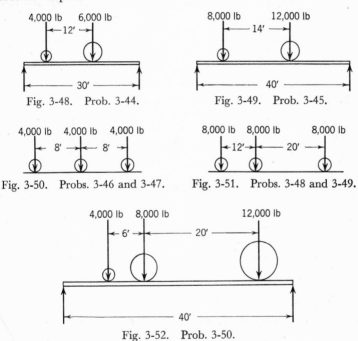

4,000 lb   6,000 lb
←—12'—→

30'

Fig. 3-48.   Prob. 3-44.

8,000 lb   12,000 lb
←—— 14' ——→

40'

Fig. 3-49.   Prob. 3-45.

4,000 lb   4,000 lb   4,000 lb
←— 8' —→←— 8' —→

Fig. 3-50.   Probs. 3-46 and 3-47.

8,000 lb   8,000 lb   8,000 lb
←12'→←—— 20' ——→

Fig. 3-51.   Probs. 3-48 and 3-49.

4,000 lb   8,000 lb   12,000 lb
←— 6' —→←——— 20' ———→

40'

Fig. 3-52.   Prob. 3-50.

4: Centroids and Moments of Inertia

4-1. First Moments

In the solution of many problems, terms involving the product of the length of a line and an area, or a mass and a distance from some point, line, or plane occur in the equations. These terms are called *first moments* of areas or masses because of their similarity to terms which represent the moment of a force about a point, line, or plane.

In most first-moment terms, the moment arm represents the distance of the centroid of the area to some point, line, or plane about which the moments are written, or it may be the distance of the center of gravity or mass center from the same place.

4-2. Centers of Gravity and Centroids Defined

The center of mass, or center of gravity, of a body is that point at which the entire mass of the body might be concentrated without changing the effect of the mass. At this point, an equal and oppositely directed reaction will balance the body, regardless of how it may be rotated.

To determine the center of gravity of a body by experiment, suspend the body in two different positions by attaching a cord at any given point, and then at a second point. The intersection of the lines of action for the two points of suspension will be the center of gravity of the body.

The centroid and the center of gravity of a body may or may not be the same point. If the body has a constant density throughout, they will be the same point. If, however, some portions of the body differ in density from other portions, the centroid and center of gravity are not the same point.

The location of the centroid depends only upon the geometrical form of the body. The centroid of a body is the exact geometrical center of the body. If the body is made of homogeneous material, its center of gravity will be the exact same point. If it is made of nonhomogeneous material, its center of gravity would depend upon the arrangement of the nonhomogeneous material and might be at some distance from the centroid, whereas the centroid will still be the geometrical center.

Lines and areas have no mass or volume and therefore cannot have centers of gravity; they have centroids.

4-3. Determination of the Centroid of an Area

Varignon's theorem states that about any point, the moment of a resultant force equals the sum of the moments of the component forces. Let us restate this principle in terms of areas instead of forces: About any point, the moment of an area equals the algebraic sum of the moments of the component areas.

This principle may be used to locate the centroid of any plane area by determining the distance of the centroid from each of two intersecting axes which lie in the plane of the area.

In Fig. 4-1, let A represent the total or resultant area of an irregular plane surface. Let this area be divided into an infinite number of small equal areas, a_1, a_2, a_3, etc., and let their coordinates be (x_1,y_1), (x_2,y_2), (x_3,y_3), etc. Let the

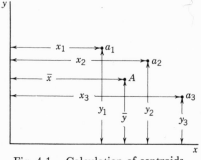

Fig. 4-1. Calculation of centroids.

coordinates of the total or resultant area A be $\bar{x}, \bar{y}$ (bar x and bar y). Applying the principle of moments to area A and its component areas,

$$A\bar{x} = a_1x_1 + a_2x_2 + a_3x_3 + \cdots + a_nx_n$$
$$A\bar{x} = ax$$
$$\bar{x} = \frac{\Sigma ax}{A}$$
$$A\bar{y} = a_1y_1 + a_2y_2 + a_3y_3 + \cdots + a_ny_n$$
$$A\bar{y} = ay$$
$$\bar{y} = \frac{\Sigma ay}{A}$$

thus locating the centroid of an area.

4-4. Centroids of Simple Geometric Areas

By geometry, the centroids of simple geometric areas are found to be as illustrated in Fig. 4-2. The centroid of a rectangle or of any parallelogram is at the intersection of its two diagonals. The centroid of a triangle is at the intersection of its medians. The centroid of a semicircle or a quarter-circle is most easily determined by integration.

Centroids of Composite Areas. A composite area is one built up of several simple areas. To determine the centroid of a

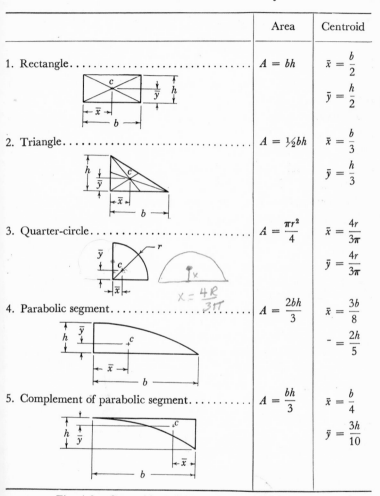

	Area	Centroid
1. Rectangle............................	$A = bh$	$\bar{x} = \dfrac{b}{2}$
		$\bar{y} = \dfrac{h}{2}$
2. Triangle...............................	$A = \frac{1}{2}bh$	$\bar{x} = \dfrac{b}{3}$
		$\bar{y} = \dfrac{h}{3}$
3. Quarter-circle.........................	$A = \dfrac{\pi r^2}{4}$	$\bar{x} = \dfrac{4r}{3\pi}$
		$\bar{y} = \dfrac{4r}{3\pi}$
4. Parabolic segment.....................	$A = \dfrac{2bh}{3}$	$\bar{x} = \dfrac{3b}{8}$
		$- = \dfrac{2h}{5}$
5. Complement of parabolic segment...........	$A = \dfrac{bh}{3}$	$\bar{x} = \dfrac{b}{4}$
		$\bar{y} = \dfrac{3h}{10}$

Fig. 4-2.   Centroids and areas of geometric surfaces.

composite area, it is divided into its simple geometric component areas. Then by applying the principle that about any axis the moment of an area equals the algebraic sum of the moments of its component areas, the centroid of the composite area is found.

4-5. Location of Centroids by Axes of Symmetry

If a surface or line is symmetric to a plane, the centroid lies in that plane.

If two or more planes of symmetry intersect in a line, that line is an axis of symmetry and contains the centroid.

If three or more planes of symmetry intersect each other in a point, the point is the centroid.

The centroids of many geometrical areas often may be located partially or completely by observation of the planes of symmetry. For example,

The centroid of a straight line is at its mid-point.

The centroid of a circle is at the center of the circle.

The centroid of a circular arc, sector, or segment is on its bisecting radius.

Example 4-1. Locate the centroid of the composite area shown in Fig. 4-3 with respect to the x and y axes.

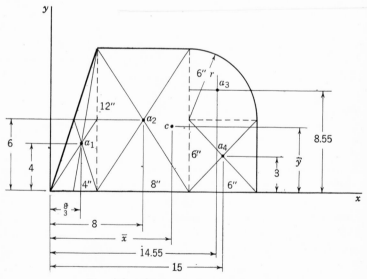

Fig. 4-3. Centroid of composite area.

SOLUTION: The composite area divides into four simple geometric areas, a triangle, two rectangles, and a quarter-circle. The total area is the resultant of these areas and passes through the centroid C of the composite area.

From the given dimensions

$$a_1 = \tfrac{1}{2}(4)(12) = 24 \text{ sq in.}$$
$$a_2 = (8)(12) = 96 \text{ sq in.}$$
$$a_3 = \tfrac{1}{4}(3.1416)(6)^2 = 28.28 \text{ sq in.}$$
$$a_4 = (6)(6) = 36 \text{ sq in.}$$

Hence

$$A = 24 + 96 + 28.28 + 36 = 184.28 \text{ sq in.}$$

To find $\bar{x}$:

$$A\bar{x} = \Sigma ax$$
$$184.28\bar{x} = (\tfrac{8}{3})24 + (8)(96) + (14.55)(28.28) + (15)(36)$$
$$\bar{x} = 9.7 \text{ in.} \quad \text{ANS.}$$

To find $\bar{y}$

$$A\bar{y} = \Sigma ay$$
$$184.28\bar{y} = (24)(4) + (96)(6)$$
$$\qquad + (28.28)(8.55) + (36)(3)$$
$$\bar{y} = 5.5 \text{ in.} \quad \text{ANS.}$$

PROBLEMS

4-1. Determine the centroid of the composite area shown in Fig. 4-4.

4-2. Determine the centroid of the cross section shown in Fig. 4-5.

4-3. Compute the distance $\bar{y}$ from the base to the centroid of the composite area of Fig. 4-6.

4-4. Determine the centroid of the disk of Fig. 4-7.

4-5. Locate the centroid of the area shown in Fig. 4-8.

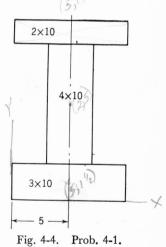

Fig. 4-4.   Prob. 4-1.

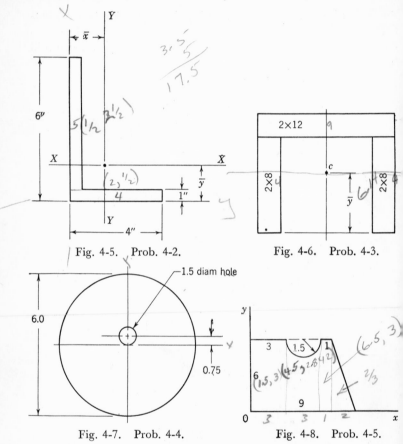

Fig. 4-5. Prob. 4-2.

Fig. 4-6. Prob. 4-3.

Fig. 4-7. Prob. 4-4.

Fig. 4-8. Prob. 4-5.

4-6. Built-up Sections

It is common engineering practice to use sections built up of standard structural-steel shapes which are riveted or welded together. Steel companies, such as United States Steel Corporation, issue handbooks listing all necessary information in table form for the various shapes. The following example will illustrate the use of handbook tables for determining the centroid of a built-up section.

Example 4-2. Determine the centroid of the built-up section shown in Fig. 4-9.

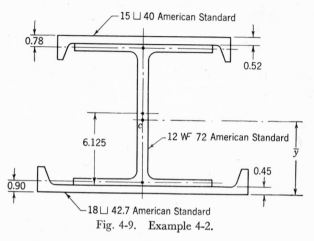

Fig. 4-9. Example 4-2.

SOLUTION: From the tables:

MEMBER	AREA, SQ IN.	CENTROID WITH RESPECT TO OWN BASE, IN.
1. 15 ⊔ 40	11.70	0.78
2. 18 ⊔ 42.7	12.48	0.90
3. 12 WF 72	21.16	6.125
Total *A*:	45.34	

Next we determine the $\bar{y}$ distance for the three members:

$y_1 = 0.45 + 12.25 + 0.52 - 0.78 = 12.44$ in. for 15 ⊔ 40
$y_2 = 0.45 + 6.125 = 6.575$ in. for 12 WF 72
$y_3 = 0.90$ in. for 18 ⊔ 42.7

Substituting,

$$A\bar{y} = \Sigma ay$$
$$45.34\bar{y} = (11.70)(12.44) + (12.48)(6.575) + (21.16)(0.90)$$
$$\bar{y} = 5.44 \text{ in.}$$

PROBLEMS

4-6. Determine the centroid of the built-up section shown in Fig. 4-10.

4-7. Determine the centroid of the built-up section shown in Fig. 4-11.

4-8. Locate the centroid of the built-up section shown in Fig. 4-12.

4-9. Locate the centroid of the built-up section shown in Fig. 4-13.

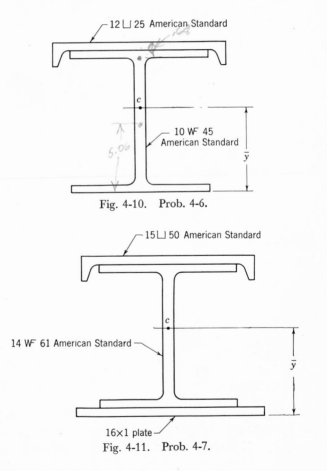

Fig. 4-10. Prob. 4-6.

Fig. 4-11. Prob. 4-7.

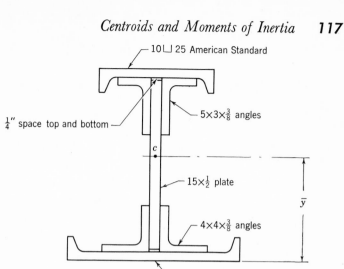

Fig. 4-12. Prob. 4-8.

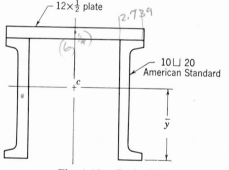

Fig. 4-13. Prob. 4-9.

4-10. Locate the centroid of a built-up section consisting of an 18-in. WF 70-lb section, with a 12-in. 30-lb channel riveted to the top of the WF beam and a 15-in. 50-lb channel riveted to the bottom.

4-7. Second Moments

When an external force is applied to a body at some distance from its axis, the body tends to rotate about that axis (Art. 3-5). In order to resist this bending moment, an internal resisting moment is set up within the body. This condition is known as the *moment of inertia* and is proportional to the cross-sectional area of the body and the square of its distance from the axis of rotation.

Expressed mathematically,

$$I_c = Ad^2$$

where I_c = moment of inertia with respect to centroidal axis
A = cross-sectional area, sq in.
d = distance from centroidal axis of rotation, in.

The unit of moment of inertia is inches to the fourth power, written in.[4] It has no physical meaning; it simply is a term indicating the relative capacity of the section to resist bending or buckling in a direction perpendicular to the reference axis.

Such terms involving the product of an area and the square of a distance have been named "moment of inertia" because of their similarity to terms which occur with rotating bodies. Strictly speaking, inertia, being a property of mass, does not apply to areas. Therefore, moment of inertia is somewhat of a misnomer when applied to areas. The term "second moment of areas" would be much more appropriate if it were not for the "inertia" of long-standing custom which demands that these terms be called moment of inertia.

4-8. Moment of Inertia of Basic Areas

By integration, the moment of inertia of some simple geometric areas are found to be as illustrated in Fig. 4-14. These and many others are usually found in handbooks.

The moment of inertia of other simple areas from which some part is removed are easily obtained from the following principle: The moment of inertia of an area with a part removed is equal to the moment of inertia of the area minus the moment of inertia of the part removed. If the axis for the area coincides with the axis of the part removed, and both are centroidal, special simple equations as illustrated in Fig. 4-15 may be written.

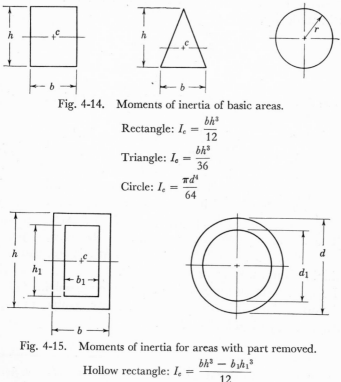

Fig. 4-14. Moments of inertia of basic areas.

$$\text{Rectangle: } I_c = \frac{bh^3}{12}$$

$$\text{Triangle: } I_c = \frac{bh^3}{36}$$

$$\text{Circle: } I_c = \frac{\pi d^4}{64}$$

Fig. 4-15. Moments of inertia for areas with part removed.

$$\text{Hollow rectangle: } I_c = \frac{bh^3 - b_1 h_1^3}{12}$$

$$\text{Hollow circle: } I_c = \frac{\pi(d^4 - d_1^4)}{64}$$

4-9. The Transfer Formula

In the solution of engineering problems, it is most usually necessary to compute the moment of inertia with respect to some axis other than the centroidal, most frequently about the base of the body. The moment of inertia is then determined by the following principle: The moment of inertia of an area with respect to any axis other than its centroidal axis is equal to the moment of inertia of the area with respect to its centroidal axis plus the product of the area and the square of the distance between the two axes. Expressed mathematically,

$$I_x = I_c + Ad^2$$
$$I_y = I_c + Ad^2$$

where I_c = moment of inertia with respect to its centroidal axis, in.[4]

A = cross-sectional area of body, sq in.

d = perpendicular distance between the two axes, in.

I_x = moment of inertia with respect to any axis x-x parallel to the horizontal centroidal axis, in.[4]

I_y = moment of inertia with respect to any axis y-y parallel to the vertical centroidal axis, in.[4]

The above equations are known as the *transfer formula* because they "transfer" the moment of inertia from the centroidal axis to some other parallel axis.

In order to facilitate solution of complex problems such as built-up sections, it is convenient to arrange results in tabular form, as shown in Fig. 4-16.

MEMBER	I_c	A	d	d^2	Ad^2	$I_x = I_c + Ad^2$

FIG. 4-16. Tabular form for solution of moment problems.

Example 4-3. Locate the centroid and determine the centroidal moment of inertia of the section shown in Fig. 4-17.

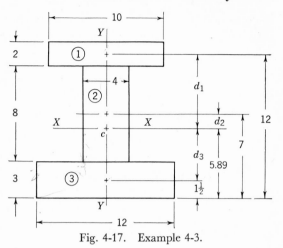

Fig. 4-17. Example 4-3.

SOLUTION: By symmetry, the centroid will be located in the Y-Y axis.

To determine $\bar{y}$:

$$A\bar{y} = \Sigma ay$$
$$88\bar{y} = (36)(\tfrac{3}{2}) + (32)(7) + (20)(12)$$
$$\bar{y} = 5.89 \text{ in.}$$

To determine centroidal moments of the individual members:

$$I_{c_1} = \frac{10 \times 2^3}{12} = 6.7 = 7 \text{ in.}^4$$

$$I_{c_2} = \frac{4 \times 8^3}{12} = 170.7 = 171 \text{ in.}^4$$

$$I_{c_3} = \frac{12 \times 3^3}{12} = 27 \text{ in.}^4$$

MEMBER	I_c	A	d	d^2	Ad^2	$I_x = I_c + Ad^2$
10- by 2-in. beam	7	20	6.11	37	740	747
4- by 8-in. beam	171	32	1.11	12	384	555
12- by 3-in. beam	27	36	4.39	19	684	711
Total I_x............	...	...	....	...	...	2,013 in.^{4}

Example 4-4.   Determine the moment of inertia of the cross section of Fig. 4-17 with respect to the *X-X* axis about its base.

SOLUTION:

MEMBER	I_c	A	d	d^2	Ad^2	$I_x = I_c + Ad^2$
10- by 2-in. beam	7	20	12	144	2,880	2,887
4- by 8-in. beam	171	32	7	49	1,568	1,739
12- by 3-in. beam	27	36	1.5	2.25	81	108
Total I_x........	...	...	....	......	.....	4,734 in.⁴

Close study of the results obtained in the foregoing two examples will reveal that the moment of inertia of an area is always least with respect to a centroidal axis.

Example 4-5.   Determine the moment of inertia of the built-up section shown in Fig. 4-9 about the base *x-x*.

SOLUTION:

MEMBER	I_c	A	d	d^2	Ad^2	$I_x = I_cAd^2$
15 ⊔ 40	9.3	11.7	11.99	143.8	1,682.5	1,691.8
12 WF 72	597.4	21.16	7.025	49.4	1,045.3	1,642.7
18 ⊔ 42.7	15.0	12.48	0.9	0.81	10.11	25.1
Total I_x....	.....	......	....	......	....	3,359.6 in.⁴

I_c and A are determined from the tables, d from the sketch.

PROBLEMS

4-11. Locate the centroidal axes *X-X* and *Y-Y* and compute the moments of inertia I_x and I_y of the unequal angle shown in Fig. 4-18. Check answers against values given in tables.

——4-12. Locate the centroidal *X-X* axis and compute the moment of inertia of the area shown in Fig. 4-19.

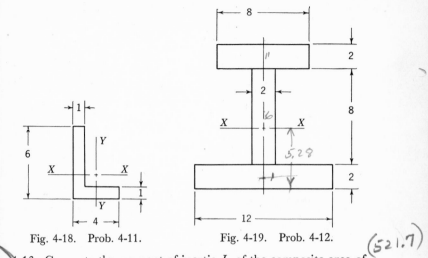

Fig. 4-18. Prob. 4-11. Fig. 4-19. Prob. 4-12.

4-13. Compute the moment of inertia I_y of the composite area of Fig. 4-6 about its centroidal axis X-X.

4-14. Determine the moments of inertia I_x and I_y of the area shown in Fig. 4-8 about the O-Y and O-X axes.

In the following problems, use handbook tables.

4-15. Determine the moment of inertia of the built-up section shown in Fig. 4-10 about its base.

4-16. Compute the moment of inertia I_x of the section shown in Fig. 4-11 about the centroidal axis and also about its base.

4-17. Compute the moment of inertia I_x of the built-up section of Fig. 4-12 about its base.

4-18. Determine the moment of inertia I_x about the centroidal axis of the section shown in Fig. 4-20.

4-19. Determine the moment of inertia I_x of the section shown in Fig. 4-20 about its base.

4-20. An 18 I 70 American Standard beam has a 12- by $\frac{1}{2}$-in. plate riveted to its top flange as shown in Fig. 4-21. Compute the moment of inertia I_x with respect to the centroidal axis.

4-21. A 12-by 1-in. plate is riveted to two 10 ⊔ 20 channels as shown in Fig. 4-22. Determine the moment of inertia I_x about the base.

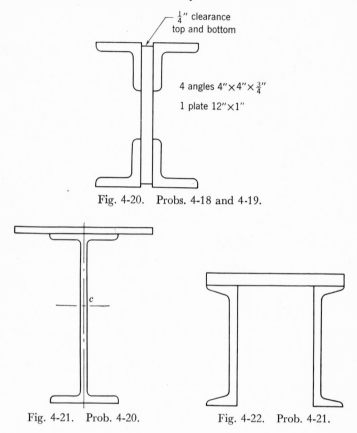

$\frac{1}{4}''$ clearance
top and bottom

4 angles 4"×4"×$\frac{3}{4}$"

1 plate 12"×1"

Fig. 4-20. Probs. 4-18 and 4-19.

c

Fig. 4-21. Prob. 4-20.

Fig. 4-22. Prob. 4-21.

$$5: \text{ Stresses in Beams}$$

5-1. Distribution of Fiber Stress

A loaded beam tends to bend, with the fibers in the concave section being in compression and those in the convex
section being in tension. The resultant compressive stress
equals the resultant tensile stress, the two forces forming a
couple, the moment of which equals the product of either force
multiplied by the distance between them. This moment is
equal to and opposite the bending moment (Art. 3-5).

The compressive stress is distributed over the entire upper
portion, and the tensile stress is distributed over the lower

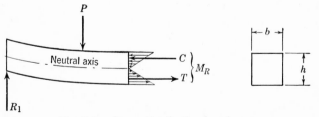

Fig. 5-1.   Stress distribution in a beam.

portion. Between them, there is a neutral axis in which the
fibers suffer no deformation along the length of the beam.
This neutral axis coincides with the centroidal axis of every
cross section of the beam, since the C and T forces must be

equal because they form a couple.   It is customary to assume
that the unit stress at any section varies directly as the distance
from the neutral axis.

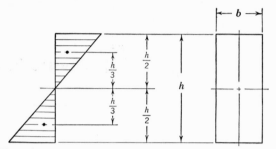

Fig. 5-2.   Enlarged view of section of rectangular beam.

Figure 5-2 shows an enlarged view of section *A-A* of a
rectangular beam.   If *s* is the maximum allowable unit stress
at the extreme fibers, both tension and compression, then
s/2 is the average unit stress.   The area under compression
A_c is ½*h* × *b*, or *bh*/2.   Similarly, $A_t = bh/2$.

Since $P = As$, total strength in compression is

$$P_c = \frac{bh}{2} \times \frac{s}{2} = \frac{sbh}{4}$$

Total strength in tension is

$$P_t = \frac{bh}{2} \times \frac{s}{2} = \frac{sbh}{4}$$

Resisting moment in compression is

$$M_{R_c} = \frac{sbh}{4} \times \frac{h}{3} = \frac{sbh^2}{12}$$

Resisting moment in tension is

$$M_{R_t} = \frac{sbh}{4} \times \frac{h}{3} = \frac{sbh^2}{12}$$

Total resisting moment is

$$M_R = M_{R_c} + M_{R_t} = 2 \times \frac{sbh^2}{12} = \frac{sbh^2}{6}$$

For equilibrium, external bending moment equals internal resisting moment:

$$M = M_R = \frac{sbh^2}{6}$$

The expression $M = sbh^2/6$ is called the *flexure formula* for rectangular sections. Since s is in pounds per square inch, b and h in inches, the unit for M must be

$$\frac{\text{lb} \times \text{in.} \times \text{in.}^2}{\text{in.}^2} = \text{in.-lb}$$

If the expression $M = sbh^2/6$ is multiplied and divided by $h/2$,

$$M = \frac{(sbh^2/6) \times (h/2)}{h/2} = \frac{sbh^3/12}{h/2}$$

but $bh^3/12$ is the moment of inertia of a rectangular section. Therefore

$$M = \frac{sI}{h/2}$$

Let $h/2 = c$, then $M = sI/c$, which is the flexure formula for steel beams.

This formula may also be written in the form $M/s = I/c$.

The quantity I/c is called the *section modulus* and is a measure of the comparative strength of beams. With a given allowable stress and length of span, the allowable load is directly proportional to the section modulus.

The values of the section moduli for structural-steel shapes are given in the handbooks of the steel manufacturers and also in the AISC handbook. Most of these handbooks use S for section modulus instead of I/c.

5-2. Conditions Involved in the Use of the Flexure Formula

The derivation of the flexure formula was accomplished with the aid of the following assumptions:

1. The unit stress and unit strain vary directly as the distance from the neutral axis.

2. The resultant compressive stress and the resultant tensile stress are equal in magnitude and opposite in direction and together form a couple.

3. The modulus of elasticity in compression is equal to the modulus of elasticity in tension.

4. The unit stresses developed do not exceed the proportional limit of the material.

5. The beam is of uniform cross section and homogeneous throughout its length.

6. The beam is straight before applying the loads.

7. The beam has sufficient transverse width relative to its length, so that there is no twisting or buckling of the beam as it bends.

8. All transverse planes perpendicular to the longitudinal axis of the beam remain plane after the beam is bent.

9. The cross section of the beam has an axis of symmetry. This axis is perpendicular to the axis about which the beam bends.

10. The applied loads must be static or gradually applied.

Most beams of one material conform approximately to the conditions on which the flexure formula is based. Hence, the flexure formula may be safely used to determine bending stresses in most beams. Moreover, the flexure formula is applied frequently to beams that do not satisfy the conditions necessary to make it valid. This practice can be justified if the amount of error is known approximately and allowance is made for the error by reducing the working stress or increasing the safety factor accordingly.

Example 5-1.   Determine the maximum flexure stress on a section of a 2- by 10-in. timber beam if the bending moment at that section is 2,400 lb-ft.   Consider the 10-in. side of the beam as being vertical.

SOLUTION: The flexure formula for rectangular beams is

$$M = \frac{sbh^2}{6}$$

Rearranging and substituting,

$$s = \frac{6M}{bh^2} = \frac{6(2,400 \times 12)}{2 \times 100}$$

$$s = 860 \text{ psi}$$

PROBLEMS

5-1. Determine the maximum flexure stress on the mid-section of a 4-in. wide by 12-in. deep beam with 12 ft between supports which carries a uniform load of 1,000 lb per ft.

5-2. What maximum uniform load can a 2- by 10-in. beam withstand if its length between supports is 14 ft and the maximum allowable stress is 1,200 psi?

5-3. A 2.5-in.-diam shaft 4 ft long supports two loads of 4,000 lb each, located 6 in. from each end.   Determine the maximum unit stress attained.

5-4. Determine how far apart 2- by 12-in. floor joists with a 14-ft span can be placed if the floor is to carry a uniform weight of 200 psf and the flexural unit stress is not to exceed 1,200 psi.

5-5. Determine the size of a square shaft which will support the loading in Prob. 5-3.

5-3. Shearing Stress in Beams

At any point in a beam where there is a direct vertical shear stress, there is also a horizontal shear stress of the same unit intensity.   The presence of horizontal shear stress is illustrated in Fig. 5-3.   Both beams have the exact same over-all dimensions, beam *a* consisting of three planks, while beam *b* is solid, and both are loaded with the same concentric load *P* similarly placed on the beams.   The three planks of beam *a* will move or slip relative to each other. Since beam *b* is solid, there can be no slipping; consequently, horizontal shear stresses are developed in its material.

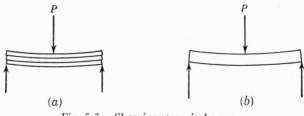

Fig. 5-3. Shearing stress in beams.

It can be shown by integration that the shearing stress is

$$s_s = 1.5 \frac{V}{A}$$

where V = vertical shear
A = cross-sectional area, sq in.

For structural-steel shapes, the AISC in its 1952 handbook recommends the following formula for calculating the total allowable shear:

$$V = 13{,}000dt$$

where d = thickness of web
t = total depth of beam

5-4. Design of Beams

Since beams develop both flexural and shear stresses, it is necessary when designing a beam for a given loading to make certain that neither type of stress exceeds the allowable limit for the material being used.

Generally, the flexural stress determines the size of beam, and so it is customary to design beams to carry the given loading with a safe flexural stress. The selected beam is then investigated to determine that it does not develop excessive shear stress at any point.   If it exceeds the maximum allowable shear stress, the beam must be redesigned using shear as the controlling stress.

The following procedure may be used for the design of beams:

1. Determine beam reactions.

2. Calculate vertical shear and plot the shear diagram.

3. Determine points of zero shear and calculate maximum bending moment.   (Maximum bending moment may be positive or negative according to type of loading and type of supports.)

4. Using the equation $M/s = I/c$, determine the value of I/c.

5. For structural-steel beams, $s = 18,000$ psi.

6. From a steel handbook, select a beam having a section modulus equal to or greater than the one computed.

Generally, when the beam carries a distributed load, the weight of the beam is included in the distributed load.   If allowance for the weight of the beam is not made in this manner, it must be added to the original loads and a new computation for maximum bending moment made.   A new I/c value is then determined.   If the new section modulus is smaller than the previous calculated one, the beam is satisfactory.   If it is larger, the beam is unsatisfactory and a slightly larger section must be used.

7. For rectangular wooden beams, the flexure formula $M/s = bh^2/6$ must be used.   Since there is no handbook for wood as there is for steel, because of the great variety of woods, b and h may be determined by substituting values for one and solving for the other in terms of the substituted value.

Also, the unit working stress will vary for different kinds of wood because of the varying strengths of the different kinds of wood.   Therefore, the unit working stress is found from the previously derived formula (Art. 1-11) $S_w = S_u/N$.

132 *Stresses in Beams*

8. Check that the section does not exceed the allowable limit for shear stress.

Example 5-2. Select an American Standard steel I beam to meet the specifications as shown in Fig. 5-4.

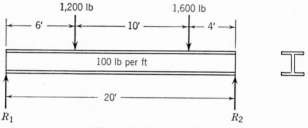

Fig. 5-4. Example 5-2.

SOLUTION:

1. Calculation of reactions:
$$\Sigma M_{R_2} = 0$$
$$20_{R_1} = (1,200)14 + (1,600)4 + (200)(20)(10)$$
$$R_1 = 2,160 \text{ lb}$$
$$\Sigma M_{R_1} = 0$$
$$20_{R_2} = (1,200)6 + (1,600)16 + (200)(20)(10)$$
$$R_2 = 2,640 \text{ lb}$$

Check:

$$\Sigma F_Y = 0$$
$$2,160 + 2,640 = 1,200 + 1,600 + 2,000$$
$$4,800 = 4,800$$

2. Vertical shear:

At R_1: $\qquad V_{R_1} = \qquad 0$
$$\underline{+2,160}$$
To right of R_1: $\quad V_{R_1} = \overline{+2,160}$
$$\underline{- \quad 600}$$
To left of 6 ft: $\quad V_6 = +1,560$
$$\underline{-1,200}$$
To right of 6 ft: $\quad V_6 = + \quad 360$
$$\underline{-1,000}$$

To left of 16 ft: $V_{16} = -\ \ 640$
$\underline{\hphantom{V_{16} = }-1,600}$
To right of 16 ft: $V_{16} = -2,240$
$\underline{\hphantom{V_{16} = }-\ \ 400}$
To left of R_2: $V_{R_2} = -2,640$
$\underline{\hphantom{V_{R_2} = }+2,640}$
At R_2: $V_{R_2} = \hphantom{+2,64}0$

3. Points of zero shear (from R_1):

$$X_1 = 0$$
$$X_2 = 6 + {}^{360}\!/_{100} = 9.6 \text{ ft}$$
$$X_3 = 20 \text{ ft}$$

4. Vertical-shear diagram (see Fig. 5-5).

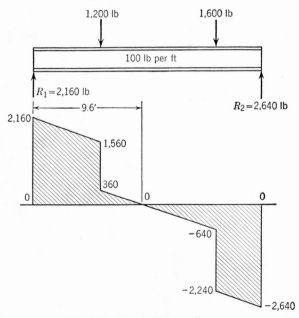

Fig. 5-5.   Vertical-shear diagram.

5. Maximum bending moment occurs at point 9.6 ft from left reaction:

$$M_{9.6} = (2,160)(9.6) - (1,200)(3.6) - (100)(9.6)(4.8)$$
$$M_{9.6} = 11,800 \text{ lb-ft} = 11,800 \times 12 = 141,700 \text{ lb-in.}$$

6. Substituting in flexure formula,

$$\frac{M}{s} = \frac{I}{c}$$

$$\frac{I}{c} = \frac{141,700}{18,000} = 7.87 \text{ in.}^3$$

7. In the tables for I beams, the next higher section modulus is 7.9 in.^{3}; therefore a 6 I 14.75 beam is required.
8. Checking for horizontal shear,

$$V_{max} = 13,000dt = (13,000)(6)(0.343)$$
$$V_{max} = 26,750 \text{ lb}$$

which is far greater than the maximum shear actually developed. Therefore the beam is satisfactory.

Example 5-3.   Design a rectangular wooden beam of white pine to be used under the following conditions:

> Maximum bending moment = 12,000 lb-ft
> Ultimate strength = 4,800 lb

Beam to be used under steady stress condition.

SOLUTION:

1. Safe working stress:

$$S_w = \frac{S_u}{N} = \frac{4,800}{8} = 600 \text{ psi}$$

2. Flexure formula for rectangular sections:

$$\frac{M}{s} = \frac{bh^2}{6}$$

$$\frac{12,000 \times 12}{600} = \frac{bh^2}{6}$$

$$\frac{bh^2}{6} = 240$$

3. Substituting values for h and solving for b:

Let $h = 6$ in.

$$\frac{36b}{6} = 240$$

$$b = 40 \text{ in.}$$

Let $h = 12$ in.

$$\frac{144b}{6} = 240$$

$$b = 10 \text{ in.}$$

Let $h = 8$ in.

$$\frac{64b}{6} = 240$$

$$b = 22.5 \text{ in.}$$

Let $h = 10$ in.

$$\frac{100b}{6} = 240$$

$$b = 14.4 \text{ in.}$$

Therefore, the sizes may be 6 by 40, 10 by 12, 8 by 24, and 10 by 16 in. The most practical size would be 10 by 12 in.

PROBLEMS

5-6–5-9. Select American Standard steel beams to meet specifications as shown in Figs. 5-6–5-9. In each case, the weight of the beam is included in the uniform load.

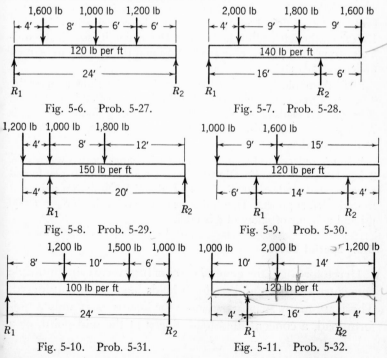

Fig. 5-6.   Prob. 5-27.

Fig. 5-7.   Prob. 5-28.

Fig. 5-8.   Prob. 5-29.

Fig. 5-9.   Prob. 5-30.

Fig. 5-10.   Prob. 5-31.

Fig. 5-11.   Prob. 5-32.

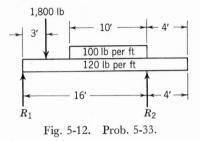

Fig. 5-12. Prob. 5-33.

5-10–5-12. Select American Standard WF beams to meet the requirements as shown in Figs. 5-10–5-12. The weight of the beam is included in the uniform load.

5-13. Design a white oak beam with a 20-ft span which is to carry a uniformly distributed load of 80 lb per ft. The beam is to be used under a steady stress condition, and its ultimate strength is 8,000 psi.

5-14. An 18-ft yellow pine beam supported at both ends is to carry a uniformly distributed load of 60 lb per ft and concentrated loads of 800, 1,000, and 1,200 lb located, respectively, 4, 8, and 12 ft from the left end of the beam. Determine its size, if the ultimate strength of yellow pine is 5,600 psi and the beam is to be used under a steady stress condition.

5-15. A maple beam 14 ft long overhangs its right support by 3 ft. It is to carry a uniformly distributed load of 50 lb per ft and concentrated loads of 900 lb at each end. If its ultimate strength is 7,600 psi and it is to be used under a steady stress, determine its commercial size.

5-16. A red cedar beam 16 ft long overhangs both supports by 2 ft. It carries a uniformly distributed load of 100 lb per ft and concentrated loads of 800 lb at each end and 1,200 lb at a point 4 ft from the left support. Determine its commercial size if $S_u = 6,000$ psi and a factor of safety of 8 is used.

5-5. Special Cases

Heretofore only the general cases of beams carrying multiple concentrated loads and uniform loads have been considered. There are many structures where the beams carry only a uniform load, a concentrated load placed at the mid-point, or a combination of both. In such cases, the computations are considerably simplified by use of the following formulas.

For a simple beam with concentrated load at its mid-point, as shown in Fig. 5-13, the reactions R_1 and R_2 are equal to

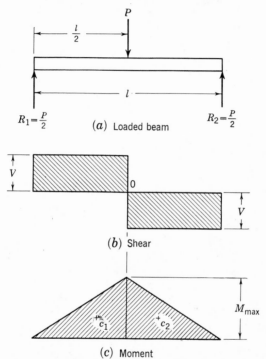

Fig. 5-13. Simple beam—concentrated load at mid-point.

$P/2$. The bending moment at any point x is

$$M_x = R_{1_x} - P(x - a)$$

At the mid-point:
$$M = R_1\left(\frac{l}{2}\right)$$

$$M = \left(\frac{P}{2}\right)\left(\frac{l}{2}\right)$$

$$M = \frac{Pl}{4}$$

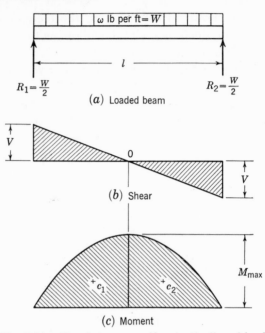

Fig. 5-14. Simple beam—uniformly distributed load.

For a simple beam with uniform load, as shown in Fig. 5-14, the reactions R_1 and R_2 are equal to $W/2$. The maximum bending moment will be at the mid-point:

$$M = R_1 \left(\frac{l}{2}\right) - \left(\frac{W}{2}\right)\left(\frac{l}{4}\right)$$
$$M = \left(\frac{W}{2}\right)\left(\frac{l}{2}\right) - \left(\frac{W}{2}\right)\left(\frac{l}{4}\right)$$
$$M = \frac{Wl}{8}$$

For a simple beam with concentrated load at mid-point and uniformly distributed load, as shown in Fig. 5-15, the reactions

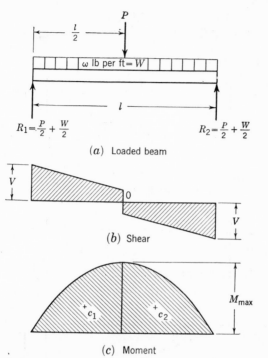

Fig. 5-15. Simple beam—concentrated load at mid-point and uniform load.

R_1 and R_2 equal $p/2 + W/2$. The maximum bending moment is

$$M = R_1\left(\frac{l}{2}\right) - \left(\frac{W}{2}\right)\left(\frac{l}{4}\right)$$

$$M = \left(\frac{P}{2} + \frac{W}{2}\right)\frac{l}{2} - \frac{Wl}{8}$$

$$M = \frac{Pl}{4} + \frac{Wl}{4} - \frac{Wl}{8}$$

$$M = \frac{Pl}{4} + \frac{Wl}{8}$$

For a cantilever beam with concentrated load at unsupported end, as shown in Fig. 5-16, the reaction R equals P.

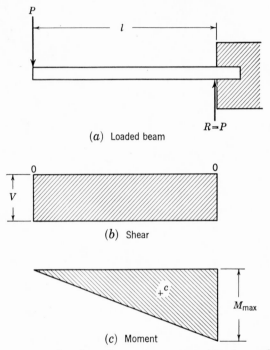

(*a*) Loaded beam

(*b*) Shear

(*c*) Moment

Fig. 5-16.   Cantilever beam—concentrated load at end.

The maximum bending moment is

$$M = -Pl$$

For a cantilever beam with uniform load, as shown in Fig. 5-17, the maximum bending moment is

$$M = \frac{-Wl}{2}$$

For a cantilever beam with concentrated load at its unsup-

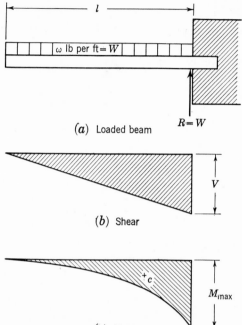

(*a*) Loaded beam $R = W$

(*b*) Shear

(*c*) Moment

Fig. 5-17. Cantilever beam—uniform load.

ported end and uniform load,

$$M = -\left(Pl + \frac{Wl}{2}\right) = -Pl - \frac{Wl}{2}$$

Example 5-4.   Determine the I beam required to meet the specifications shown in Fig. 5-18.

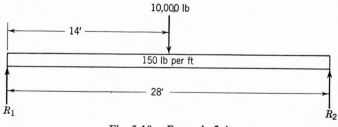

Fig. 5-18.   Example 5-4.

SOLUTION: Given

$$P = 10,000 \text{ lb} \qquad W = 150 \times 28 = 4,200 \text{ lb}$$

Maximum bending moment:

$$M = \frac{Pl}{4} + \frac{Wl}{8}$$

$$M = \frac{(10,000)28}{4} + \frac{(4,200)28}{8} = 84,700 \text{ lb-ft} = 1,016,000 \text{ lb-in.}$$

Flexure formula for steel beams:

$$\frac{M}{s} = \frac{I}{c}$$

$$\frac{1,016,000}{18,000} = \frac{I}{c}$$

$$\frac{I}{c} = 56.5 \text{ in.}^3$$

In the tables for I beams, the next higher section modulus is 58.9 in.³, which corresponds to a 15 I 42.9 beam.

The weight of the beam itself is

$$42.9 \times 28 = 1,200 \text{ lb}$$

The added bending moment is

$$\frac{1,200 \times 28 \times 12}{8} = 50,400 \text{ lb-in.}$$

The added value of I/c is

$$\frac{50,400}{18,000} = 2.8 \text{ in.}^3$$

The required value of I/c is

$$56.5 + 2.8 = 59.3 \text{ in.}^3$$

In the tables for I beams, the next higher section modulus is 60.5 in.³, which corresponds to a 15 I 45 beam.

Checking for horizontal shear:

$$V_{max} = 13,000dt = (13,000)(15)(0.452)$$
$$V_{max} = 88,140 \text{ lb}$$

Actual maximum shear developed:

$$V = R_1 = \tfrac{1}{2}(P + W) = \tfrac{1}{2}(10,000 + 5,400)$$
$$V = 7,700 \text{ lb}$$

Since the actual shear developed is well under the maximum, the beam is safe.

Example 5-5. A balcony projecting 8 ft from a wall is to be supported by white oak beams spaced 3 ft apart. It is to support a maximum load of 150 lb per sq ft of floor area including the weight of the beams. Calculate the size of beams required if the ultimate strength of white oak is 8,000 psi and the allowable horizontal shear is 125 psi.

SOLUTION: Each beam acting as a cantilever supports $8 \times 3 = 24$ sq ft. of load.

$$\text{Total load } W = 24 \times 150 = 36,000 \text{ lb}$$

Maximum bending moment for cantilever beam with uniform load:

$$M = \frac{-Wl}{2} = \frac{3,600 \times 8}{2} = -14,400 \text{ lb-ft} = -172,800 \text{ lb-in.}$$

Safe working stress:

$$S_w = \frac{S_u}{N} = \frac{8,000}{8} = 1,000 \text{ psi}$$

Flexure formula for rectangular sections:

$$\frac{M}{s} = \frac{bh^2}{6}$$

$$\frac{172,800}{1,000} = \frac{bh^2}{6}$$

$$\frac{bh^2}{6} = 172.8 \text{ in.}^3$$

Substituting values for h and solving for b,

Let $h = 6$ in.	Let $h = 8$ in.
$\dfrac{36b}{6} = 172.8$	$\dfrac{64b}{6} = 172.8$
$b = 28.8$ in.	$b = 16.2$ in.

Let $h = 10$ in.	Let $h = 12$ in.
$\dfrac{100b}{6} = 172.8$	$\dfrac{144b}{6} = 172.8$
$b = 10.3$ in.	$b = 7.2$ in.

Commercial sizes are 6 by 30, 8 by 18, 10 by 12, 12 by 8 in.

Therefore 12 by 8 in. is the most economical commercial size. Checking for horizontal shear,

$$V = R = 3,600 \text{ lb}$$

Shearing stress formula:

$$S_s = \frac{1.5V}{A} = \frac{(1.5)(3,600)}{(12)(8)} = 52.5 \text{ psi}$$

The shearing stress developed is well under the maximum and therefore the beam is safe.

Example 5-6.   A floor carrying a load of 100 lb per sq ft of floor area including the weight of the floor is supported by 6- by 10-in. white pine beams 15 ft long.   Calculate the spacing required if the ultimate strength of white pine is 5,600 psi, allowable shearing stress is 85 psi, and the density of wood is 40 lb per cu ft.

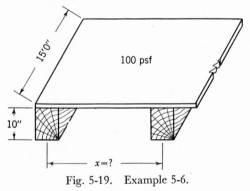

Fig. 5-19.   Example 5-6.

SOLUTION: Each beam must support a floor area of $15X$ sq ft.   Each beam weighs

$$(40)(15)\left(\frac{10 \times 6}{144}\right) = 250 \text{ lb}$$

Total weight $W = (100)15X + 250 = 1,500X + 250$

Safe working stress:

$$S_w = \frac{S_u}{N} = \frac{5,600}{8} = 700 \text{ psi}$$

Maximum bending moment:

$$M = \frac{Wl}{8} = \frac{(1,500X + 250)(15)(12)}{8} = 33,800X + 5,700$$

Flexure formula:

$$\frac{M}{s} = \frac{bh^2}{6}$$
$$\frac{33,800X + 5,700}{700} = \frac{6(10)^2}{6}$$
$$48.3X + 8.2 = 100$$
$$X = 1.92 \text{ ft} = 23 \text{ in.}$$

Checking for horizontal shear:
Total weight on each beam

$$W = (1,500)(1.9) + 250 = 2,850 \text{ lb}$$

Maximum vertical shear

$$V = \frac{R}{2} = \frac{2,850}{2} = 1,425 \text{ lb}$$

Substituting,

$$S_s = \frac{1.5V}{A} = \frac{(1.5)(1,425)}{(10)(6)} = 35.6 \text{ psi}$$

Since the allowable shearing stress is 85 psi, the spacing is safe.

PROBLEMS

5-17. Select an American Standard beam for a span of 24 ft to carry a uniformly distributed load of 200 lb per ft, not including its own weight, and a load of 6,000 lb concentrated at its mid-point.

5-18. Select an American Standard I beam to be used in a floor supporting a load of 300 lb per sq ft of floor area including the weight of the floor. The span is to be 20 ft, and the beams are to be spaced 2 ft apart, center to center.

5-19. Compute the maximum spacing of 16 WF 45 American Standard beams to support a load of 350 lb per sq ft of floor area with a span of 24 ft.

5-20. A cantilever beam 10 ft long is to support a uniformly distributed load of 100 lb per ft not including its own weight, and a concentrated load of 1,000 lb at its free end. Select a wide-flange section to carry the load.

5-21. Select an American Standard beam for a span of 25 ft to carry a uniformly distributed floor load of 500 lb per sq ft of floor area and to be spaced 18 in. apart, center to center.

5-22. Select two American Standard channels, placed back to back, to carry the same load as that given in Prob. 5-6. (HINT: Each channel must have a value of I/c equal to or greater than one-half of the computed section modulus.)

5-23. Select an American Standard wide-flange beam for a span of 36 ft to carry a superimposed uniformly distributed load of 500 lb per linear ft and a load of 5,000 lb concentrated at its mid-point.

5-24. A 16 WF 45 American Standard beam carries a uniformly distributed load of 1,000 lb per ft, not including its own weight, over a span of 24 ft. What is the maximum unit stress developed? Is the design safe?

5-25. Calculate the size of white oak beam with a span of 18 ft required to support a uniform load of 200 lb per linear ft, including its own weight.

5-26. A white pine beam with a 16-ft span carries a uniformly distributed load of 250 lb per ft including its own weight and a load of 2,000 lb concentrated at its mid-point. Determine the size of cross section required.

5-27. Determine the size of a square white oak beam used as a cantilever 8 ft long carrying a load of 1,000 lb at its free end and a uniformly distributed load of 150 lb per ft, not including its own weight. Density of wood is 40 lb per cu ft.

5-28. A floor, supported by white oak beams with a span of 14 ft and spaced 2 ft apart, center to center, carries a load of 100 lb per sq ft of floor area including its own weight. Calculate the size of beam required.

5-29. Determine the spacing required for 2- by 12-in. joists 16 ft long to carry a floor load of 100 lb per sq ft of floor area, including the weight of the joints. Assume an allowable stress of 1,000 psi.

5-30. A balcony projecting 8 ft from the wall is to be supported by yellow birch beams 8 by 12 in. in cross section, spaced 24 in. apart. If the ultimate strength of yellow birch is 6,640 psi and allowable horizontal shear is 125 psi, calculate the maximum allowable uniform load which the balcony may safely sustain.

5-31. A floor carries a load of 100 lb per sq ft of floor area including its own weight. If the supporting beams are of yellow birch with a span of 14 ft and spaced 28 in. apart, center to center, determine their dimensions if the depth (h) is twice the width (b). Assume the density of yellow birch to be 40 lb per cu ft.

5-32. Compute the spacing of 10 I 35 American Standard beams to support a uniformly distributed load of 400 lb per sq ft of floor area with a span of 20 ft.

5-33. A cantilever beam 10 ft long is to support a superimposed load of 80 lb per linear ft and a concentrated load of 500 lb at its free end. Select two equal-angle sections to be placed back to back forming a T beam to carry the load (see hint, Prob. 5-22).

5-34. A simple beam 30 ft long has a cross section as shown in Fig. 4-20. Determine the total allowable uniformly distributed load, including the weight of the beam.

5-35. A simple beam 24 ft long has a cross section as shown in Fig. 4-11. What is the maximum allowable load concentrated at its mid-point?

5-6. Stresses above the Elastic Limit. Modulus of Rupture

The flexure formula $M/s = I/c$ is derived from the assumption that the unit fiber stresses are no greater than the elastic limit of the material. If the load on a beam is increased, until the stress in the outer fibers exceeds the elastic limit, unit stress will no longer be proportional to unit deformation, and the stress distribution will differ from that shown in Figs. 5-1 and 5-2. The approximate variation of unit fiber stress at the rupture stage is shown in Fig. 5-20. It is apparent that the

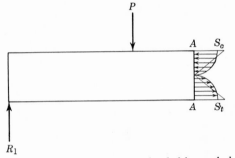

Fig. 5-20.   Stress distribution for beam loaded beyond elastic limit.

unit stress is not proportional to the unit strain except near the neutral axis, and therefore unit stress does not vary directly as the distance from the neutral axis. Consequently, the resisting moment in a beam stressed beyond its elastic limit is larger than that found from the flexure formula. Thus, if the ultimate strength of the material is substituted for s in the flexure formula $M/s = I/c$, the resulting value of M will be less than the maximum moment that the beam can resist. Therefore the flexure formula is not valid for stresses beyond the elastic limit. However, in the case of materials which rupture, it is customary to compute a value of s by means of the flexure formula, $s = Mc/I$ in which M is the value of the moment just preceding rupture. This value of s is not a true unit stress, but it is a measure of the rupture strength of a material and consequently is called the *modulus of rupture* of the material. It is useful solely as a comparison of strength of beams of same material and shape.

PROBLEMS

5-36. A timber beam 8 in. wide by 16 in. deep and 12 ft long supported at both ends broke under a load at its mid-point of 104,300 lb. Compute its modulus of rupture, neglecting the weight of the beam.

5-37. A cast-iron test bar 2 in. wide by 1¼ in. deep and 8 in. long broke under a load of 10,200 lb. Compute its modulus of rupture.

5-38. The modulus of rupture of a piece of plate glass was found to be 3,200 psi. If its dimensions were 12 in. wide by ½ in. thick and 2 ft long, what was the load at its mid-point which caused it to break?

6: Deflections in Beams

6-1. Introduction

When a beam is loaded with transverse loads (Art. 5-1), compressive stresses occur on one side of the neutral axis and tensile stresses on the other side. The fibers subjected to compression are shortened; those subjected to tension are elongated. This causes the beam to curve or deflect from its original unstressed position.

This deflection depends upon (1) the loads acting on the beam, (2) the dimensions of the beam, and (3) the stiffness of the material of which the beam is made. The stiffness of the material is measured by the modulus of elasticity of the material (Art. 1-8).

The relative importance of the amount of deflection in a beam depends upon the purpose which the beam is to serve. For many beams the amount of deflection is unimportant, the only requirement being that the beam carry the applied loads without developing stresses which exceed the safe limiting values. However, for many beams, such as shafting which carries pulleys and gears and beams that support plastered ceilings or machinery, the amount of deformation under load is important. In some cases, it is the maximum deflection rather than the fiber stress which governs the dimensions of a beam.

6-2. Radius of Curvature

The same assumptions which were made in deriving the flexure formula are made in the development of the theory of deflections (Art. 5-2).

When a beam bends, its neutral axis becomes a curve which is known as the *elastic curve*. The *radius of curvature* at any point on the elastic curve equals the radius of the circle drawn tangent to the curve at that point.

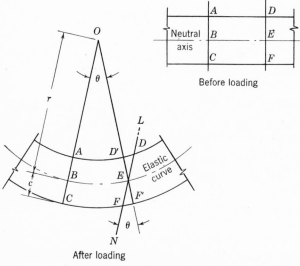

Before loading

After loading

Fig. 6-1. Radius of curvature.

Figure 6-1 represents a small portion of a beam acted upon by two equal and opposite couples M. Sections ABC and DEF are two planes which, prior to loading, were parallel and the distance BE apart. When the beam is loaded, plane DEF rotates with respect to plane ABC to a position $D'EF'$. Passing plane LN through E parallel to ABC shows that the upper fiber AD has been compressed an amount DD', the bottom fiber CF elongated an amount FF', and the intermediate fibers strained in direct proportion to their distances from the neutral axis. Since the sectors EFF' and OBE are similar,

$$\frac{EF}{OB} = \frac{FF'}{BE}$$

But unit strain, ϵ, incurred in fiber CF while elongating it to length CF' is $\epsilon = FF'/BE$; EF is the distance from the neutral axis to the outer fiber, denoted by C; and OB is the radius of curvature at B or E. Therefore

$$\frac{C}{r} = \epsilon$$

or

$$r = \frac{C}{\epsilon}$$

From our study in axially loaded members, $\epsilon = s/E$; and from the flexure formula, $C = sI/M$. Substituting,

$$r = \frac{sI/M}{s/E} = \frac{sI}{M} \times \frac{E}{s}$$
$$r = \frac{EI}{M}$$

or

$$M = \frac{EI}{r}$$

where r = radius of curvature of the elastic curve at a section for which the bending moment is M

E = modulus of elasticity of material of beam

I = moment of inertia of cross section

These relations make it possible to determine the radius of curvature of the elastic curve at any point on a beam if the bending moment is known or to determine the bending moment necessary to bend a beam to a given radius of curvature.

PROBLEMS

6-1. A steel band saw is 0.05 in. thick and 1.50 in. wide. Determine the diameter pulley which should be used to limit the flexural stress in the saw blade to 25,000 psi. ($E = 3 \times 10^7$ psi)

6-2. Wire is usually coiled on drums directly from rolling mills. Does a $\frac{1}{4}$-in.-diam copper wire receive any permanent deformation if it is coiled on drums 3 ft in diameter? ($E = 15 \times 10^6$ psi)

6-3. Calculate the radius of curvature at the center portion of the steel beam loaded as shown in Fig. 6-2.

$(I = 48 \text{ in.}^4, E = 3 \times 10^7 \text{ psi})$

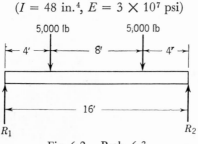

Fig. 6-2. Prob. 6-3.

6-4. A timber cantilever beam 2 by 12 in. by 10 ft long supports a uniformly distributed load of 20 lb per linear ft, including its own weight. What is the radius of curvature at the fixed end when the 2-in. side is used as the depth? The 12-in. side?

$(E = 15 \times 10^5 \text{ psi})$

6-3. Slopes and Deflections

There are several methods available for calculating the slope and deflection of a beam at any point. The moment-area method is one of the most popular because of its simplicity.

The *slope* of the elastic curve at any point is the angle (θ) which the tangent to the curve makes with the horizontal, or neutral axis, at the given point. In Fig. 6-3, θ is the slope at the point *A*.

The deflection of a beam at any section is equal to the vertical distance (y) at the section between the elastic curve and the horizontal, or neutral axis.   In Fig. 6-3, y is the deflection of the beam at section A-A.

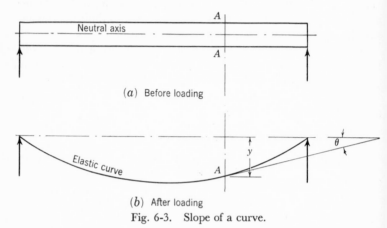

(a) Before loading

(b) After loading

Fig. 6-3.   Slope of a curve.

Figure 6-4 shows the elastic curve of a loaded beam greatly exaggerated.   A very short length Δl is laid off on the elastic curve and perpendiculars erected at its extremities, A and B, which intersect at the point O, making a very small angle $\Delta\theta$. Since the distance between A and B is very small, the radius of curvature r and the bending moment M may be considered identical for both points.

The length of the elastic curve of ordinary beams is very nearly the same as the horizontal length of the unloaded beam. Thus, $\Delta l = \Delta X$, which is its horizontal projection.

But $\Delta l = r\Delta\theta$, and $r = EI/M$.   Substituting and solving for $\Delta\theta$,

$$\Delta X = \frac{EI}{M} \Delta\theta$$

$$\Delta\theta = \frac{M}{EI} \Delta X$$

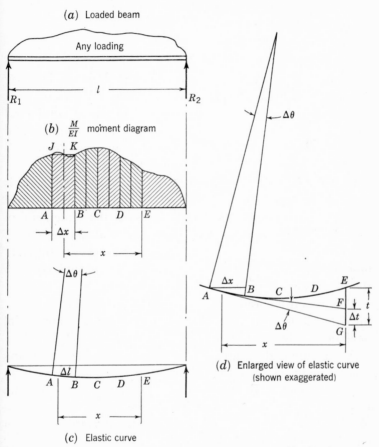

Fig. 6-4. (*a*) Loaded beam. (*b*) Moment diagram. (*c*) Elastic curve.
(*d*) Enlarged view of elastic curve (shown exaggerated).

By construction, the change in slope from A to B equals $\Delta\theta$.
Therefore, the change in slope from A to B equals $(M/EI)\,\Delta X$.
Similarly, the change in slope from B to C, C to D, and
D to E is also equal to $(M/EI)\,\Delta X$. Therefore, by summing
up these individual slopes, we obtain the total change in slope
from A to E as

$$\theta = \sum_{A}^{E} \Delta\theta = \sum_{A}^{E} \frac{M}{EI} \Delta X$$

On the right-hand side of this equation, M is the bending moment for any ΔX between A and E. Since ΔX is such a very small length, its corresponding moment M can be considered constant in value for every ΔX length. This equation also shows that each M ordinate of the bending-moment diagram is reduced in height by its corresponding EI factor.

Furthermore, the product of M/EI times ΔX (Fig. 6-4b) is equal to the area of the rectangle $ABJK$ and also to the change in slope over length ΔX. This leads to the statement of theorem 1 of the moment-area method for calculating slopes:

The change in slope (in radians) between tangents drawn at any two points on the elastic curve of a loaded beam is equal to the M/EI area between these two points.

The second theorem which leads to the method of calculating deflections by moment areas involves the use of tangential deviations. By definition:

A tangential deviation is the vertical distance from any point A on the elastic curve of a beam to a tangent drawn from any other point. In Fig. 6-5, $T_{A/B}$ is the tangential deviation at point A with respect to B; $T_{B/A}$ is the tangential deviation at B with respect to A. In general, such deviations are not equal, as can be seen in Fig. 6-5.

Referring once more to Fig. 6-4d, t is the tangential deviation at E with respect to A; and Δt, which is located an average distance X from ΔX, is a very small part of t. Since points A and B are a very short distance apart, the tangents AG and BF drawn at these two points may be considered equal, and $\Delta t = \overline{AG} \, \Delta\theta$. Moreover, since the amount of deflection in beams is very slight, provided they are not stressed beyond their allowable limits, the tangents AG and BF may be set equal to X without appreciable error. Therefore

$$\Delta t = X \Delta \theta$$

Since $\Delta\theta = (M/EI) \Delta X$, substituting gives

$$\Delta t = X \frac{M}{EI} \Delta X$$

This expression for Δt pertains to any two adjacent points on the elastic curve. Thus, if tangents from points C and D are extended, the value of each Δt between points G and E will be

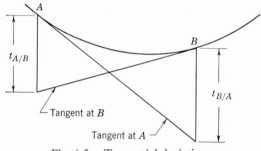

Fig. 6-5. Tangential deviations.

equal to this same general expression, and the sum of these individual Δt's will equal the tangential deviation at E with respect to A. Mathematically,

$$t_{E/A} = \sum_{A}^{E} \Delta t = \sum_{A}^{E} X \frac{M}{EI} \Delta X$$

On the right-hand side of this equation, the expression $(M/EI) \Delta X$ may be recognized as the rectangular area previously used to obtain theorem 1. The value of X is the average distance between this area and the point at which the tangential deviation is desired.

The $(M/EI) \Delta X$ areas may be grouped together into sections, the areas and centroids of which may be readily obtained. The summation of the products of these areas and the distance from the centroid of the area to the point in question then yields the value of the tangential deviation. Thus

$$t_{E/A} = \overline{X} \sum_{A}^{E} \frac{M}{EI} \Delta X$$

where $\overline{X}$ is the distance between the centroid of the M/EI area and the point at which the tangential deviation is desired. This leads to the statement of theorem 2 of the moment-area method for calculating beam deflections:

The tangential deviation between any two points on the elastic curve of a loaded beam is equal to the moment of the area of the M/EI diagram between those two points taken about the point where the tangential deviation is desired.

It must be noted that when moments are taken of M/EI areas, the algebraic signs will be the same as those of the M/EI areas being considered. Thus, the moments of positive M/EI areas will be positive and those of negative areas will be negative.

Theorems 1 and 2 and their related equations may be used to develop formulas to obtain the slopes and deflections at any point on the elastic curve of any loaded beam. We shall develop the formulas for the maximum slopes and maximum deflections for the four most common types of beam loadings, which are (1) cantilever beam with concentrated load at free end, (2) simple beam with concentrated load at mid-point, (3) cantilever beam with uniformly distributed load, and (4) simple beam with uniformly distributed load.

6-4. Cantilever Beam with Concentrated Load at Free End

The cantilever beam of Fig. 6-6 is acted upon by a concentrated load at its free end. The fixed end of cantilever beams is generally assumed to be horizontal, so that a tangent drawn to the elastic curve at the wall will be horizontal, and consequently will have a zero slope. The slope will increase until it reaches a maximum at the free end of the beam, where the angle which the tangent to the elastic curve makes with the

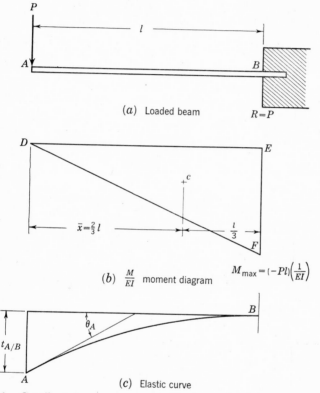

(a) Loaded beam

(b) $\frac{M}{EI}$ moment diagram $M_{max} = (-Pl)\left(\frac{1}{EI}\right)$

(c) Elastic curve

Fig. 6-6. Cantilever beam—concentrated load at end. (a) Loaded beam. (b) Moment diagram. (c) Elastic curve.

horizontal is greatest. By theorem 1, this is equal to area *DEF*. Thus

$$\theta = \left(\frac{l}{2}\right)\left(\frac{Pl}{EI}\right) = \frac{Pl^2}{2EI} \qquad \text{radians}$$

The tangential deviation of point *A* with respect to *B* is equal to the vertical distance from *A* to the tangent drawn from B. But a tangent at B is horizontal. Therefore, the tangential deviation $t_{A/B}$ is equal to the deflection Δ (delta) of the beam.

$$\Delta = t_{A/B} = \left(-\frac{Pl}{EI}\right)\left(\frac{l}{2}\right)\left(\frac{2l}{3}\right) = -\frac{Pl^3}{3EI} \quad \text{in.}$$

The negative sign indicates that the M/EI area is negative.

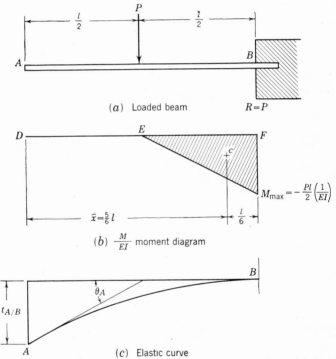

(a) Loaded beam $R = P$

(b) $\dfrac{M}{EI}$ moment diagram

(c) Elastic curve

Fig. 6-7. Cantilever beam—concentrated load at mid-point. *(a)* Loaded beam. *(b)* Moment diagram. *(c)* Elastic curve.

If the load P is placed at the mid-point of the cantilever beam (Fig. 6-7), then

$$\Delta = t_{A/B} = \left(-\frac{Pl}{2EI}\right)\left(\frac{1}{2} \times \frac{l}{2}\right)\left(\frac{5}{6}l\right) = \frac{-5Pl^3}{48EI} \quad \text{in.}$$

It is obvious that this deflection is less than that obtained when the load was placed at the free end of the cantilever beam.

Example 6-1. Determine the maximum deflection and slope for the cantilever wooden beam 4 in. wide by 10 in. deep of Fig. 6-8 ($E = 15 \times 10^5$ psi).

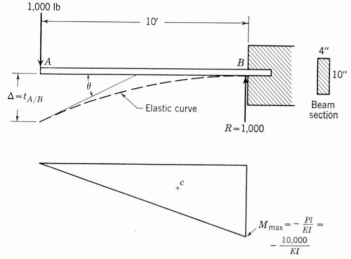

Fig. 6-8.

SOLUTION: The moment of inertia for rectangular sections is

$$I = \frac{bh^3}{12}$$

Therefore

$$I = \frac{4 \times 10^3}{12} = \frac{10^3}{3} \text{ in.}^4$$

Substituting,

$$\Delta = \frac{-Pl^3}{3EI}$$

$$\Delta = \frac{-10^3(10^3 \times 12^3)}{3(15 \times 10^5)(10^3/3)}$$

$$\Delta = -1.15 \text{ in.} \qquad \text{(maximum deflection)}$$

The formula for slope:

$$\theta = \frac{Pl^2}{2EI}$$

Substituting,

$$\theta = \frac{10^3(10^2 \times 12^2)}{2(15 \times 10^5)(10^3/3)}$$

$$\theta = 0.015 \text{ radian}$$

6-5. Simple Beam with Concentrated Load at Mid-point

The simple beam of Fig. 6-9 is acted upon by a concentrated load P at its mid-point. The maximum slope of the beam is

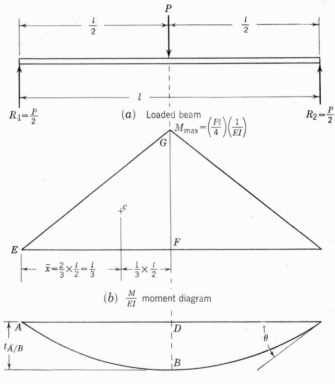

Fig. 6-9. Simple beam—concentrated load at mid-point. (a) Loaded beam. (b) Moment diagram. (c) Elastic curve.

at its reaction points, since the angle which the tangent to the curve makes with the horizontal is greatest at the reaction points. By theorem 1 this is equal to area EFG. Therefore

$$\theta = \frac{1}{2}\left(\frac{Pl}{4} \times \frac{1}{EI}\right)\frac{l}{2} = \frac{Pl^2}{16EI} \qquad \text{radians}$$

The point of zero slope, and hence of maximum deflection, is at the mid-point, since, from symmetry, the tangent at the mid-point of the elastic curve is horizontal. But this is the definition of the tangential deviation of point A with respect to B. Therefore

$$\Delta = t_{A/B} = \left(\frac{2}{3} \cdot \frac{l}{2}\right)\left(\frac{1}{2} \cdot \frac{Pl}{4EI}\right)\left(\frac{l}{2}\right)$$

$$\Delta = \frac{Pl^3}{48EI} \qquad \text{in.}$$

6-6. Beams Subjected to Uniform Loads

The difference in the method of calculating slopes and deflections of uniformly loaded beams and that of beams carrying concentrated loads is in the location of the proper centroids of the curved moment diagrams. In Art. 3-5, it was shown that the bending-moment equation for beams which are subjected to uniform loads is of the second degree, and hence the moment diagram is parabolic. Figure 4-2 is a table of the centroids and areas of various geometric surfaces, of which Nos. 4 and 5 are of particular interest at this time, since they are of the same shape as the moment diagrams of a simple beam and cantilever beam, respectively, with uniformly distributed loads (see Figs. 5-14 and 5-17). The location of the centroids of the moment diagrams being now established, we may proceed with types 3 and 4 of beam loadings.

6-7. Cantilever Beam. Uniformly Distributed Load

The slope at point B is zero and at point A is a maximum. Therefore the slope at A is equal to the area of the M/EI dia-

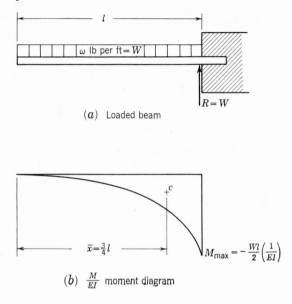

(*a*)   Loaded beam

(*b*) $\frac{M}{EI}$ moment diagram

(*c*)   Elastic curve

Fig. 6-10. Cantilever beam—uniform load. (*a*) Loaded beam. (*b*) Moment diagram. (*c*) Elastic curve.

gram between A and B (Fig. 6-10):

$$\theta = \left(\frac{l}{3}\right)\left(\frac{Wl}{2EI}\right) = \frac{Wl^2}{6EI} \qquad \text{radians}$$

The maximum deflection of the beam is equal to the tangential deviation $t_{A/B}$.

$$\Delta = t_{A/B} = \left(\frac{l}{3}\right)\left(-\frac{Wl}{2EI}\right)\left(\frac{3l}{4}\right) = -\frac{Wl^3}{8EI} \qquad \text{in.}$$

6-8. Simple Beam. Uniform Load

The maximum slope is at the reaction points and is therefore equal to area EFG:

$$\theta = \left(\frac{2}{3}\right)\left(\frac{l}{2}\right)\left(\frac{Wl}{8EI}\right) = \frac{Wl^2}{24EI} \qquad \text{radians}$$

The maximum deflection is equal to the tangential deviation $t_{A/B}$:

$$\Delta = t_{A/B} = \left(\frac{5}{8} \times \frac{l}{2}\right)\left(\frac{2}{3} \times \frac{Wl}{8EI}\right)\left(\frac{l}{2}\right) = \frac{5Wl^3}{384EI} \qquad \text{in.}$$

For convenience, the expressions for maximum slope and deflection for the simple and cantilever beams which have just been derived, are shown in Table 6-1.

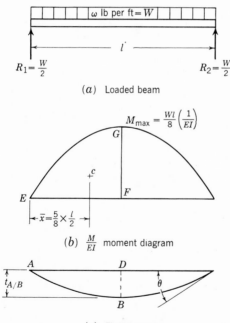

(*a*) Loaded beam

(*b*) $\frac{M}{EI}$ moment diagram

(*c*) Elastic curve

Fig. 6-11.   Simple beam—uniform load.   (*a*) Loaded beam.   (*b*) Moment diagram.   (*c*) Elastic curve.

Table 6-1.   *Maximum Bending Moment, Slope, and Deflection Formulas*

TYPE OF BEAM AND LOADING	MAXIMUM BENDING MOMENT (M)	MAXIMUM SLOPE (θ)	MAXIMUM DEFLECTION
Simple beam, concentrated load at mid-point	$M = \dfrac{Pl}{4}$	$\theta = \dfrac{Pl^2}{16EI}$	$\Delta = \dfrac{Pl^3}{48EI}$
Cantilever beam, concentrated load at free end	$M = Pl$	$\theta = \dfrac{Pl^2}{2EI}$	$\Delta = \dfrac{Pl^3}{3EI}$
Simple beam, uniform load	$M = \dfrac{Wl}{8}$	$\theta = \dfrac{Wl^2}{24EI}$	$\Delta = \dfrac{5Wl^3}{384EI}$
Cantilever beam, uniform load	$M = \dfrac{Wl}{2}$	$\theta = \dfrac{Wl^2}{6EI}$	$\Delta = \dfrac{Wl^3}{8EI}$

where P = concentrated load, lb

W = total uniform load, lb $(W = wl)$

l = length in feet (change to inches in formulas)

E = modulus of elasticity, psi

I = moment of inertia, in.^{4}

θ = maximum slope, radians

Δ = maximum deflection, in.

M = maximum bending moment, lb-in.

When a beam is loaded with both a uniformly distributed load and one concentrated at its mid-point, the total deflection is found by calculating the deflection due to each load separately and adding the results.

In buildings, the maximum deflection is usually limited to $\frac{1}{360}$ of the span of the beam.

Example 6-2.   Calculate the deflection of a 10 I 40 American Standard beam with a 10-ft span having a uniformly distributed load of 1,000 lb per ft.   Is the beam safe if the maximum allowable deflection is limited to $\frac{1}{360}$ of its span?

SOLUTION: For uniform load:

$$\Delta = \frac{5Wl^3}{384EI} = \frac{5(1,000)(10)(10 \times 12)^3}{(384)(30,000,000)(158)}$$

$$\Delta = 0.047 \text{ in.}$$

Maximum allowable deflection:

$$\Delta = \tfrac{1}{360}(10)(12) = 0.333 \text{ in.}$$

Therefore the beam is safe.

Example 6-3.   Calculate the deflection for the beam of Example 5-4.   If the maximum deflection is limited to $\tfrac{1}{360}$ of the span of the beam, determine if it is safe.   If not safe, determine the lightest safe beam to use.

SOLUTION: The beam as previously calculated is a 15 I 45 American Standard with a moment of inertia of 453.6 in.[4].

Deflection formula for concentrated load at mid-point:

$$\Delta = \frac{Pl^3}{48EI} = \frac{(10,000)(28 \times 12)^3}{(48)(30,000,000)(453.6)}$$

$$\Delta = 0.580 \text{ in.}$$

Deflection formula for uniform load:

$$\Delta = \frac{5Wl^3}{48EI} = \frac{5(195)(28)(28 \times 12)^3}{(48)(30,000,000)(453.6)}$$

$$\Delta = 1.580 \text{ in.}$$

$$\text{Total deflection} = 1.580 + 0.580 = 2.160 \text{ in.}$$

Maximum allowable deflection $= (\tfrac{1}{360})(28)(12) = 0.933 \text{ in.}$

Therefore the beam is not safe.

To determine the beam with a maximum deflection of 0.933 in.,

$$\Delta = \frac{Pl^3}{48EI} + \frac{5Wl^3}{48EI} = \frac{Pl^3 + 5Wl^3}{48EI} = \frac{l^3(P + 5W)}{48EI}$$

$$0.933 = \frac{(28 \times 12)^3(10,000 + 5 \times 195 \times 28)}{(48)(30,000,000)I}$$

$$I = 1,050 \text{ in.}[4]$$

The next higher moment of inertia is 1,169.5 in.[4], corresponding to a 20 I 65.4 American Standard beam.   This beam is 20.4 lb per ft heavier than that as previously calculated.   Recalculating the bending moment,

Added bending moment:

$$M = \frac{(20.4)(28)(28)(12)}{8} = 2,400 \text{ lb-in.}$$

Added value of $\dfrac{I}{c} = \dfrac{2,400}{18,000} = 0.133$ in.^{3}

This added value is of no consequence, and therefore the beam is safe.

PROBLEMS

6-5. Calculate the deflection of a white oak beam which supports a uniformly distributed load of 100 lb per linear ft over a span of 14 ft. The beam is 4 in. wide by 8 in. deep. The modulus of elasticity of white oak is 1,800,000 psi.

6-6. Calculate the deflection of a yellow poplar beam used as a cantilever supporting a uniformly distributed load of 80 lb per ft including its own weight, and a load of 500 lb concentrated at its free end. The beam is 6 in. wide by 8 in. deep and projects 10 ft from the support. The modulus of elasticity of white poplar is 1,500,000 psi.

6-7. Calculate the deflection of a 10 I 35 American Standard beam with a 20-ft span which supports a load of 2,000 lb at its mid-point.

6-8–6-15. Calculate the deflection for the beams of Probs. 5-17–5-24. If the maximum deflection is limited to $\frac{1}{360}$ of the span, determine in each case if the beam is safe. If not safe, calculate the lightest safe beam to use.

6-16. A 4-in.-diam steel shaft resting on bearings 6 ft apart carries a 5-ton flywheel. If the maximum deflection is not to exceed $\frac{1}{360}$ of the span, is it safe?

6-17–6-21. Calculate the deflection for the beams of Probs. 5-27–5-32. In each case, if the maximum deflection is limited to $\frac{1}{360}$ of the span, determine if the beam is safe. If not safe, redesign the beam to a safe size. The modulus of elasticity of white oak is 1,800,000 psi and of yellow birch 2,000,000 psi.

6-22. Wood floor joists 2 by 12 in. by 16 ft long are spaced 14 in. apart. Determine the load per square foot of floor area including the weight of beam and floor which may be applied. Assume $E = 1,500,000$ psi.

7: Statically Indeterminate Beams

7-1. Introduction

The beams considered in the preceding chapters were held in equilibrium by external forces which formed a system of parallel forces in a plane. The equations of equilibrium, $\Sigma F_y = 0$ and $\Sigma M = 0$ were sufficient for calculating the reactions at the supports, since there were not more than two supports and therefore not more than two unknown external forces acting on the beam. In other words, the force systems acting on simple, cantilever, and overhanging beams are *statically determinate*. Moreover, these beams are assumed to rest on supports which offer no restraint, thus allowing normal deflection of the beams.

Whenever the normal deflection of a beam is prevented, restraining moments are induced. The reactions cannot be calculated from the equations of equilibrium alone, since the number of unknown reactions is more than the number of equations of equilibrium. Such beams are known as *statically indeterminate*. To find the reactions, use is made of an additional relation between the external forces and the elastic deformation produced by them.

Figure 7-1 shows a comparison of a cantilever beam and a beam fixed at one end and supported at the other end. It is evident that the latter beam would become a cantilever if the support, R_2, were removed. This support prevents a normal deflection of the beam and induces a restraining moment M at the wall. Thus, there are three unknowns, R_1, R_2, and M, but

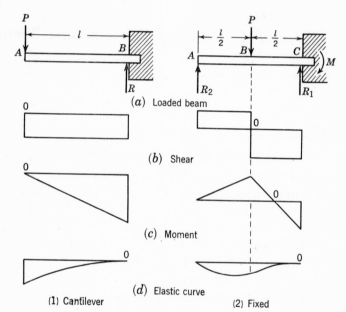

Fig. 7-1. Comparison of cantilever with beam fixed at one end and supported at other end. (a) Loaded beam. (b) Shear. (c) Moment. (d) Elastic curve.

only two available equations of equilibrium, $\Sigma F_y = 0$ and $\Sigma M = 0$. This is the reason for calling these beams *statically indeterminate*. An additional condition is required for solution of the system. Usually, this additional condition is that the deflection under the support is zero.

If a beam is fixed at both ends, there are two restraining moments induced, one at each end; consequently two additional equations will be needed unless the beam is symmetrically loaded. In the latter case, there will be one additional equation necessary for solution.

The principle of superposition affords a simple solution of fixed beams, since it makes use of the deflections of simple and cantilever beams which have been previously established.

This principle may be stated as follows: The deflection at any point in a fixed beam is the algebraic sum of two deflections: (1) the deflection due to the load alone, with the end restraints relaxed, and (2) the deflection due to the end restraints along, with the load removed.

7-2. Beam Fixed at One End with Concentrated Load at Mid-point

In Art. 6-4 it was shown that the deflection at the free end of a cantilever beam with a concentrated load P at the end is $\Delta = -\ Pl^3/3EI$. If the end is not free to deflect because of a support R_2 placed at that end, then R_2 must be a force which would cause an upward deflection equal to $+Pl^3/3EI$ if it were acting alone on the end of the cantilever. Since $R_2 = P$,

$$\Delta = \frac{R_2 l^3}{3EI}$$

It also was shown in Art. 6-4 that the deflection due to a concentrated load at the mid-point of the cantilever beam was

$$\Delta = -\ \frac{5Pl^3}{48EI}$$

Applying the principle of superposition as an equation,

$$\frac{R_2 l^3}{3EI} - \frac{5Pl^3}{48EI} = 0$$

from which

$$R_2 = \frac{5P}{16}$$

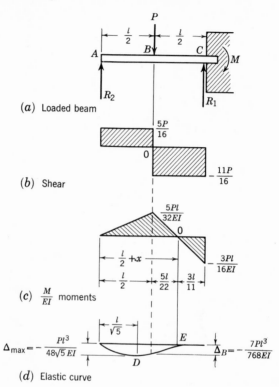

(a) Loaded beam

(b) Shear

(c) $\dfrac{M}{EI}$ moments

(d) Elastic curve

Fig. 7-2.   Beam fixed at one end, supported at other end, concentrated load at mid-point.   (a) Loaded beam.   (b) Shear.   (c) Moments.   (d) Elastic curve.

After R_2 has been determined, R_1 and M may be found by the equations of static equilibrium:

$$R_1 + R_2 = P \qquad (\Sigma F_y = 0)$$
$$R_1 = P - \tfrac{5}{16}P = \tfrac{11}{16}P$$
$$M_B = R_2\left(\frac{l}{2}\right) = \frac{5P}{16}\left(\frac{l}{2}\right) = \frac{5Pl}{32}$$
$$M_C = R_2 l - P\left(\frac{l}{2}\right) = \frac{5Pl}{16} - \frac{Pl}{2} = \frac{5Pl}{16} - \frac{8Pl}{16} = -\frac{3Pl}{16}$$

A point of inflection occurs at the point where the moment is zero:

$$\Sigma M_E = R_2 \left(\frac{l}{2} + X\right) - PX = 0$$

$$\frac{5P}{16}\left(\frac{l + 2X}{2}\right) - PX = 0$$

$$\frac{5l}{32} + \frac{5X}{16} - X = 0$$

$$X = \frac{5l}{22} \qquad \text{to the right of load } P$$

The deflection under the load P is obtained by computing the tangential deviation at B with respect to C:

$$\Delta = t_{B/C} = \left(\frac{5Pl}{32EI}\right)\left(\frac{1}{2} \times \frac{5l}{22}\right)\left(\frac{1}{3} \times \frac{5l}{22}\right)$$

$$- \left(\frac{3Pl}{16EI}\right)\left(\frac{1}{2} \times \frac{3l}{22}\right)\left(\frac{5l}{22} + \frac{2}{3} \times \frac{3l}{11}\right)$$

$$\Delta = \frac{(125 - 972)Pl^3}{32 \times 2 \times 22 \times 3 \times 22EI} = -\frac{7 \times 11 \times 11Pl^3}{32 \times 4 \times 11 \times 6 \times 11}$$

$$= -\frac{7Pl^3}{768EI} = \frac{0.0091Pl^3}{EI}$$

Since there is only one restraining moment acting on the beam, the point of maximum deflection will be off center in a direction away from the fixed end. This point may be found by equating the moments of the M/EI areas on either side of it about points A and C, for the tangential deviations obtained in this manner are equal. This equation will locate the point of maximum deflection $l/\sqrt{5}$ from the supported end.

The maximum deflection at this point is

$$\Delta = \frac{Pl^3}{48\sqrt{5}\,EI} = \frac{0.0093Pl^3}{EI}$$

Comparison with the deflection under the load will show that the maximum deflection is just 0.0002 greater. As a percentage, this is two-hundredths of one per cent!

7-3. Beam Fixed at One End with Uniform Load

Figure 7-3 shows a beam which is fixed at one end and supported at the other end with a uniformly distributed load. If the support, R_2, were removed, the beam would become a cantilever. The uniform load W would cause the free end to

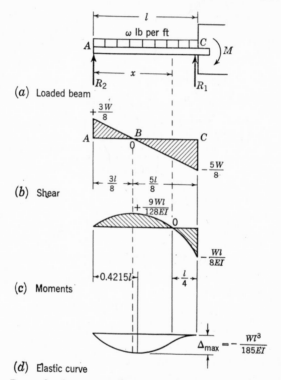

(a) Loaded beam

(b) Shear

(c) Moments

(d) Elastic curve

Fig. 7-3. Beam fixed at one end, supported at other end, uniformly distributed load. (*a*) Loaded beam. (*b*) Shear. (*c*) Moments. (*d*) Elastic curve.

deflect a distance $\Delta = -Wl^3/8EI$. Since the end does not deflect, R_2 must be a force which would cause an upward deflection equal to $Wl^3/8EI$ if it were acting alone on the end of the cantilever. But the deflection of a concentrated load P

on the free end of a cantilever being $\Delta = Pl^3/3EI$, and since $R_2 = P$, we have by substitution

$$\frac{R_2 l^3}{3EI} = \frac{Wl^3}{8EI}$$

from which

$$R_2 = \frac{3W}{8}$$

R_1 and M are found by statistics:

$$R_1 = W - \frac{3W}{8} = \frac{5W}{8}$$

Points of maximum bending moment occur where the shear diagram is zero. This occurs at the fixed end and at a point $\frac{5}{8}l$ from the fixed end:

$$M_B = \left(\frac{3W}{8}\right)\left(\frac{1}{2} \times \frac{3l}{8}\right) = \frac{9Wl}{128}$$

$$M_C = \left(\frac{3W}{8}\right)\left(\frac{1}{2} \times \frac{3l}{8}\right) - \left(\frac{5W}{8}\right)\left(\frac{1}{2} \times \frac{5l}{8}\right) = -\frac{Wl}{8}$$

Since the maximum bending moment is $-Wl/8$, this beam is no stronger than a simple beam similarly loaded.

A point of inflection occurs where the moment is zero:

$$R_2 X - WX\left(\frac{X}{2}\right) = 0 \qquad (\Sigma M = 0)$$

$$\frac{3WlX}{8} - \frac{WX^2}{2} = 0$$

$$\frac{X}{2} = \frac{3l}{8}$$

$$X = \frac{3l}{4}$$

The point of maximum deflection will be off center in a direction away from the fixed end. Equating the moments of the M/EI areas on either side about A and C locates the point of maximum deflection at a distance $0.4215l$ from the supported end.

The maximum deflection at this point is

$$\Delta = -\frac{Wl^3}{185EI} = -\frac{0.0054Wl^3}{EI}$$

Example 7-1.   Select an American Standard I beam 24 ft long, fixed at one end and supported at the other, which carries a uniformly distributed load of 600 lb per linear ft, including its own weight. Calculate the maximum deflection.

SOLUTION:

Maximum positive moment:

$$M = \tfrac{9}{128}Wl = \tfrac{9}{128}(14,400)(24 \times 12) = 292,000 \text{ lb-in.}$$

Maximum negative moment:

$$M = \tfrac{1}{8}Wl = \tfrac{1}{8}(14,400)(24 \times 12) = 518,000 \text{ lb-in.}$$

The flexure formula is

$$\frac{M}{s} = \frac{I}{c}$$

$$\frac{518,000}{18,000} = \frac{I}{c}$$

$$\frac{I}{c} = 28.8 \text{ in.}^3$$

The next higher section modulus in bold face is 34.1 in.³, corresponding to a 12 WF 27 beam.   The moment of inertia of this beam is 204.1 in.⁴

The deflection formula: *2 3 8*

$$\Delta = 0.0054 \frac{Wl^3}{EI} = \frac{(0.0054)(14,400)(24 \times 12)^3}{(30,000,000)(204.1)}$$

$$\Delta = 0.3 \text{ in.}$$

PROBLEMS

7-1.   Select an American Standard WF section 20 ft long fixed at one end and supported at the other which carries a load of 10,000 lb concentrated at its mid-point.   Calculate the maximum deflection.

7-2. Select an American Standard I beam 18 ft long fixed at one end and supported at the other, which carries a uniformly distributed load of 500 lb per ft not including its own weight. Maximum deflection must not exceed 0.75 in.

7-3. Select an American Standard I beam 20 ft long fixed at one end and supported at the other which carries a load of 5,000 lb concentrated at its mid-point and a uniformly distributed load of 200 lb per ft, including its own weight. Calculate the maximum deflection.

7-4. A 10-in. square timber beam 20 ft long is fixed at one end and supported at the other end. It is loaded with a uniformly distributed load of 200 lb per ft including its own weight. Calculate the maximum fiber stress (s) and the maximum deflection (Δ). Use $E = 1,500,000$ psi.

7-4. Beam Fixed at Both Ends.   Concentrated Load at Mid-point

The reactions R_1 and R_2 and the moments M_1 and M_2 (Fig. 7-4) are the four unknown quantities which make beams fixed at both ends statically indeterminate. The conditions of equilibrium give the following relation:

$$R_1 = R_2 = \frac{P}{2}$$

Because of symmetry,

$$M_1 = M_2$$

If the end restraints are temporarily removed, the beam will be a simple beam with a maximum positive bending moment of $Pl/4$ at the mid-span.   Removing the load and reapplying in turn the end restraints M_1 and M_2 gives the bending moments represented by the congruent triangles I and II, respectively, of Fig. 7-4c. Considering the end restraints together gives a bending moment represented by the rectangle consisting of the two triangles I and II. This rectangle has a constant ordinate equal to the unknown moment $M_1 = M_2$. Since the beam has a constant cross section, the moment diagram also represents the M/EI moment area.

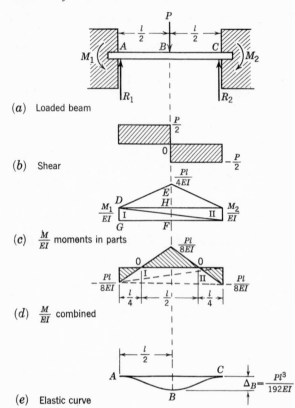

(a) Loaded beam

(b) Shear

(c) $\frac{M}{EI}$ moments in parts

(d) $\frac{M}{EI}$ combined

(e) Elastic curve

Fig. 7-4. Beam fixed at both ends, concentrated load at mid-point. (a) Loaded beam. (b) Shear. (c) Moments. (d) Combined. (e) Elastic curve.

Since both ends of the beam are completely fixed, the change in slope from A to C is zero. Applying theorem 1 of moment areas,

$$\left(\frac{Pl}{4EI} \times \frac{l}{2}\right) + \left(\frac{Ml}{EI} \times l\right) = 0$$

Solving for the unknown restraint,

$$M_1 = -\frac{Pl}{8}$$

Since $M_2 = M_1$,

$$M_2 = -\frac{Pl}{8}$$

The bending-moment diagram may be obtained by rotating the negative area of the end restraints about its upper edge. The overlapping positive and negative areas will cancel out as

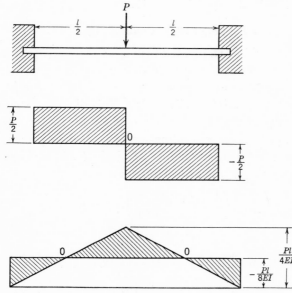

Fig. 7-5. Bending-moment diagram.

shown in Fig. 7-4d. Thus, the bending-moment diagram for a beam fixed at both ends may be drawn by beginning with the diagram for a simple beam similarly loaded. At the ends, mark off ordinates of M_1 and M_2, respectively, and connect these points with a straight line. This line will then be the zero axis. This method of constructing a bending-moment diagram for a beam fixed at both ends with a concentrated load at its mid-point is shown in Fig. 7-5.

The maximum deflection occurs at the mid-point of the

beam because the load is symmetrically placed. Making use of theorem 2 of moment areas, the deflection is equal to the moment area *DEFG*, taken about *EF*. Therefore

$$\Delta = \left(\frac{Pl}{4EI}\right)\left(\frac{1}{2} \times \frac{l}{2}\right)\left(\frac{1}{3} \times \frac{l}{2}\right) - \left(\frac{Pl}{8EI}\right)\left(\frac{l}{2}\right)\left(\frac{l}{4}\right)$$

$$= \frac{Pl^3}{96EI} - \frac{Pl^3}{64EI} = -\frac{Pl^3}{192EI}$$

7-5. Beam Fixed at Both Ends. Uniformly Loaded

As indicated in Art. 6-6, the principles of moment areas may be applied without difficulty to uniformly loaded beams.

The uniform load *W* produces the parabolic bending-moment diagram *CDHE* of Fig. 7-6c. This diagram is positive, and the maximum moment is $Wl/8EI$. Below the axis line *CEH* is the rectangular bending-moment diagram produced by the equal restraining moments M_1 and M_2. The change in slope from *A* to *B* is zero. Therefore

$$\left(\frac{Wl}{8EI}\right)\left(\frac{2}{3} \times l\right) + \left(\frac{M_1}{EI}\right)(l) = 0$$

$$M_1 = -\frac{Wl}{12EI}$$

Since $M_2 = M_1$,

$$M_2 = -\frac{Wl}{12EI}$$

The maximum deflection occurs at the mid-point and equals the moment area *CDEFG*, taken about *DF*. Thus

$$\Delta = \left(\frac{Wl}{8EI}\right)\left(\frac{2}{3} \times \frac{l}{2}\right)\left(\frac{3}{8} \times \frac{l}{2}\right) - \left(\frac{Wl}{12EI}\right)\left(\frac{l}{2}\right)\left(\frac{l}{4}\right) = 0$$

$$\Delta = -\frac{Wl^3}{384EI}$$

For convenience, the expressions for the maximum bending moments and deflections of the fixed beams of the preceding articles have been placed in Table 7-1.

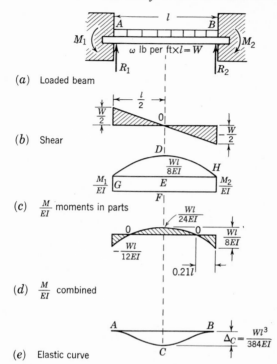

Fig. 7-6. Beam fixed at both ends, uniform load. (a) Loaded beam. (b) Shear. (c) Moments in parts. (d) Combined. (e) Elastic curve.

Table 7-1. *Maximum Bending Moments and Deflections for Fixed Beams*

TYPE OF BEAM AND LOADING	MAXIMUM BENDING MOMENT (M)	MAXIMUM DEFLECTION (Δ)
Fixed at one end, concentrated load at midpoint	$M = \dfrac{3Pl}{16}$	$\Delta = 0.0093\,\dfrac{Pl^3}{EI}$
Fixed at one end, uniform load	$M = \dfrac{-Wl}{8}$	$\Delta = 0.0054\,\dfrac{Wl^3}{EI}$
Fixed at both ends, concentrated load at midpoint	$M = \dfrac{Pl}{8}$	$\Delta = 0.0052\,\dfrac{Pl^3}{EI}$
Fixed at both ends, uniform load	$M = \dfrac{-Wl}{12}$	$\Delta = 0.0029\,\dfrac{Wl^3}{EI}$

Example 7-2.   Select an American Standard WF section 25 ft long between fixed supports to carry a load of 40,000 lb concentrated at its mid-point.   Calculate the maximum deflection.

SOLUTION: Maximum bending moment:

$$M = \frac{Pl}{8} = \frac{(40,000)(25)(12)}{8} = 1,500,000 \text{ lb-in.}$$

Flexure formula:

$$\frac{M}{s} = \frac{I}{c}$$

$$\frac{1,500,000}{18,000} = \frac{I}{c}$$

$$\frac{I}{c} = 83.3 \text{ in.}^3$$

The lightest WF section which has a section modulus greater than 83.3 in.^{3} is an 18 WF 50 section with a section modulus of 89 in.^{3}.

The added bending moment due to the weight of the beam:

$$M = \frac{Wl}{12} = \frac{(50)(25)(25 \times 12)}{12} = 32,250 \text{ lb-in.}$$

The additional section modulus will be

$$\frac{31,250}{18,000} = \frac{I}{c} = 1.7 \text{ in.}^3$$

Total $I/c = 83.3 + 1.7 = 85.0$ in.^{3}; therefore the beam is safe. Maximum deflection:

$$\Delta = \frac{(40,000)(25 \times 12)^3}{(192)(30,000,000)(800)} + \frac{(1,250)(25 \times 12)^3}{(384)(30,000,000)(800)}$$
$$\Delta = 0.55 + 0.11 = 0.66 \text{ in.}$$

PROBLEMS

7-5. Select an American Standard beam 24 ft long between fixed ends to carry a load of 30,000 lb concentrated at its mid-point and a uniformly distributed load of 200 lb per ft including its own weight.   Calculate the maximum deflection.

7-6. Select an American Standard WF section 30 ft long between fixed supports which carries a uniformly distributed load of 500 lb per linear ft not including its own weight.   What is the maximum deflection caused by the load?

7-7. Select an American Standard I beam 20 ft long between fixed ends to carry a load of 20,000 lb concentrated at its mid-point. Calculate the maximum load this beam may safely carry if the deflection is limited to $\frac{1}{360}$ of the span.

7-8. Determine the maximum fiber stress and deflection for the beam in Prob. 6-14 if the beam were fixed at both ends. $12C$

7-6.   Continuous Beams

In Fig. 7-7 is represented a continuous beam resting on four supports with a uniformly distributed load over the entire

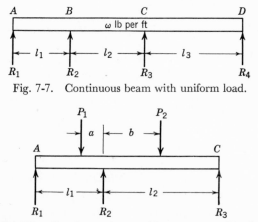

Fig. 7-7.   Continuous beam with uniform load.

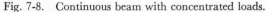

Fig. 7-8.   Continuous beam with concentrated loads.

length.   Figure 7-8 represents a continuous beam resting on three supports with concentrated loads P_1 and P_2.   These types of beams are best solved by the theorem of three moments, which gives the relation between the moments at any three successive supports.   After the moments at the supports have been obtained, the reactions may be determined.   The deflections in this type of beam are of relatively minor importance and therefore will not be determined.

The general theorem of three moments for continuous beams with uniform load is as follows:

$$M_A l_1 + 2M_B(l_1 + l_2) + M_C l_2 = -\frac{W_1 l_1^3}{4} - \frac{W_2 l_2^3}{4}$$

In case the spans and loads are equal, the theorem becomes

$$M_A + 4M_B + M_C = \frac{-Wl^2}{2}$$

where l = length of each span, ft

For continuous beams with concentrated loads the theorem of three moments is

$$M_A l_1 + 2M_B(l_1 + l_2) + M_C l_2$$
$$= \frac{P_1}{l_1}(l_1 - a)^3 + \frac{P_2}{l_2}(l_2 - b)^3 - P_1 l_1(l_1 - a) - P_2 l_2(l_2 - b)$$

If the spans and loads are equal and the loads are concentrated in the middle of its span, the theorem becomes

$$M_A + 4M_B + M_C = -\frac{3Pl}{4}$$

where P = magnitude of concentrated load

l = length of each span

The above equations give the relation between the moments at any three successive supports.   The method of solution is to write equations for supports 1, 2, and 3, supports 2, 3, and 4, etc., until the last support is used.   There will be two fewer equations than the number of unknown supports.   If there are supports at the ends of the beam, the moments at the ends are zero.   If the beam overhangs an end support, the moment at the support is determined by statics with the overhanging part being used as a free body.

After the moments at the supports have been determined, the first span is taken as a free body to determine the end reaction. The first and second spans are then taken together as a free body to determine the second reaction, etc., until finally the entire beam is taken as a free body.

After the reactions are determined, the maximum positive moments at the other danger sections are computed.

Example 7-3. A 40-ft long beam with spans of 14, 16, and 10 ft, which carry loads of 400, 200, and 500 lb per ft, respectively, is shown in Fig. 7-9. Compute the moment at each support, the reactions, and the maximum positive moments at the other danger points.

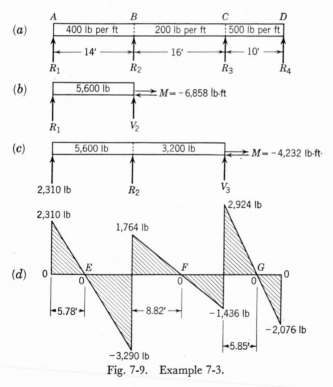

Fig. 7-9.   Example 7-3.

SOLUTION: M_A and M_D are both zero. By the general theorem of three moments:

$$M_A l_1 + 2M_B(l_1 + l_2) + M_C l_2 = -\frac{W_1 l_1^3}{4} - \frac{W_2 l_2^3}{4}$$

Substituting,

$$0 + 2M_B(14 + 16) + M_C(16) = -\frac{(400)(14)^3}{4} - \frac{(200)(16)^3}{4}$$

And

$$16M_B + 2M_C(16 + 10) + 0 = -\frac{(200)(16)^3}{4} - \frac{(500)(10)^3}{4}$$

Simplifying,

$$60M_B + 16M_C = -479{,}200$$
$$16M_B + 52M_C = -329{,}800$$

Solving the simultaneous equations,

$$M_B = -6{,}858 \text{ lb-ft}$$
$$M_C = -4{,}232 \text{ lb-ft}$$

To solve for R_1, the first span at the left is used as a free body. Figure 7-9b shows the free-body diagram, the section being cut just to the left of R_2. Taking moments about the cut section,

$$14R_1 + 6{,}858 = (5{,}600)(7)$$
$$R_1 = 2{,}310 \text{ lb}$$

The next free body consists of the first and second spans together as shown in Fig. 7-9c. The moment equation gives

$$16R_2 + (2{,}310)(30) + 4{,}232 = (5{,}600)(23) + (3{,}200)(8)$$
$$R_2 = 5{,}054 \text{ lb}$$

Since the unknown reactions have been reduced to two, the entire beam is now used as a free body. Taking moments about R_4,

$$10R_3 + (5{,}054)(26) + (2{,}310)(40) = (5{,}600)(33)$$
$$+ (3{,}200)(18) + (5{,}000)(5)$$
$$R_3 = 4{,}360 \text{ lb}$$

Again using the entire beam as a free body and taking moments about R_3,

$$10R_4 + (3,200)(8) + (5,600)(23) = (2,310)(30)$$
$$+ (5,054)(16) + (5,000)(5)$$
$$R_4 = 2,076 \text{ lb}$$

Checking by $\Sigma F_2 = 0$,

$$2,310 + 5,054 + 4,360 + 2,076 = 5,600 + 3,200 + 5,000$$
$$13,800 = 13,800$$

With all the reactions known, the shear diagram may now be drawn, as shown in Fig. 7-9d.

The other three danger points are E, F, and G.

The distance from the end of the beam to E is $2,310/400 = 5.78$ ft.

Similarly, the distance from the end of the beam to F is 22.82 ft and from the end of the beam to G is 35.85 ft.

For maximum positive moments:

$$M_{5.78} = (2,310)(5.78) - (400)(5.78)(2.89) = 6,680 \text{ lb-ft}$$
$$M_{22.82} = (2,310)(22.82) + (5,054)(8.82) - (5,600)(15.82)$$
$$- (1,764)(4.41) = 930 \text{ lb-ft}$$
$$M_{35.85} = (2,310)(35.85) + (5,054)(21.85) + (4,360)(5.85)$$
$$- (5,600)(28.85) - (3,200)(13.85) - (2,925)(2.92)$$
$$M_{35.85} = 4,306 \text{ lb-ft}$$

Another method for determining the maximum positive moments is obtained by the following theorem: The area of the shear diagram between any two points on a beam is equal to the change in moment in the beam in the same length. Since the moment at the end of the beam is zero, the area of the shear diagram up to any point is equal to the moment at that point. Using the method of the area of the shear diagram,

$$M_{5.78} = (2,310)(\tfrac{1}{2})(5.78) = 6,676 \text{ lb-ft}$$
$$M_{22.82} = 6,676 + (1,764)(\tfrac{1}{2})(8.82) - (3,290)(\tfrac{1}{2})(8.22) = 933 \text{ lb-ft}$$
$$M_{35.85} = 933 + (2,924)(\tfrac{1}{2})(5.85) - (1,436)(\tfrac{1}{2})(7.18) = 4,320 \text{ lb-ft}$$

Example 7-4.   A 40-ft long beam with four equal spans carries a load of 3,000 lb at the mid-point of each span as shown in Fig. 7-10. Compute the moments at each support, the reactions, and the maximum positive moments.

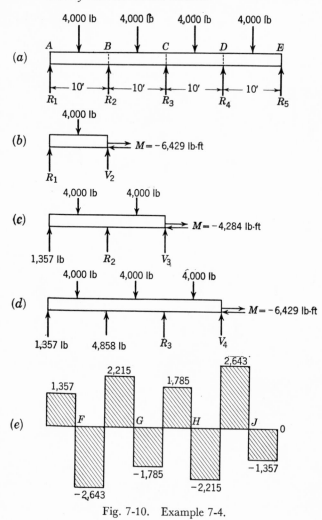

Fig. 7-10. Example 7-4.

SOLUTION: M_A and M_E are both zero. With loads and spans equal, the theorem of three moments is

$$M_A + 4M_B + M_C = -\frac{3Pl}{4}$$

Substituting,

$$0 + 4M_B + M_C = -\tfrac{3}{4}(4,000)(10)$$
$$M_B + 4M_C + M_D = -\tfrac{3}{4}(4,000)(10)$$
$$M_C + 4M_D + 0 = -\tfrac{3}{4}(4,000)(10)$$

Simplifying,

$$4M_B + M_C = -30,000$$
$$M_B + 4M_C + M_D = -30,000$$
$$M_C + 4M_D = -30,000$$

Solving three simultaneous equations in three unknowns,

$$M_B = M_D = -6,429 \text{ lb-ft}$$
$$M_C = -4,284 \text{ lb-ft}$$

To solve for R_1, the first span at the left is taken as a free body. Figure 7-10*b* shows the free-body diagram. Taking moments,

$$10R_1 + 6,429 = (4,000)5$$
$$R_1 = 1,357 \text{ lb}$$

To solve for R_2, the first and second spans are next taken as a free body. Figure 7-10*c* shows the free-body diagram. The moment equation:

$$10R_2 + (1,357)20 + 4,284 = (4,000)(15 + 5)$$
$$R_2 = 4,858 \text{ lb}$$

To solve for R_3, the first, second, and third spans are taken as a free body. Figure 7-10*d* shows the free-body diagram:

$$10R_3 + (1,357)30 + (4,858)20 + 6,429 = (4,000)(25 + 15 + 5)$$
$$R_3 = 3,570 \text{ lb}$$

Using the entire beam as a free body and taking moments about R_5,

$$10R_4 + (1,357)(40) + (4,858)30 + (3,570)20$$
$$= (4,000)(35 + 25 + 15 + 5)$$
$$R_4 = 4,858 \text{ lb}$$

Again using the entire beam as a free body and taking moments about R_4,

$$10R_5 + (4{,}000)(5 + 15 + 25) = (4{,}000)5 + (3{,}570)10$$
$$+ (4{,}858)20 + (1{,}357)30$$
$$R_5 = 1{,}357 \text{ lb}$$

Checking by $\Sigma F_2 = 0$,

$$1{,}357 + 4{,}858 + 3{,}570 + 4{,}858 + 1{,}357 = (4{,}000)4$$
$$16{,}000 = 16{,}000$$

The shear diagram may now be drawn, as shown in Fig. 7-10e. The maximum positive moments, using the method of area of shear diagram:

$$M_F = (1{,}357)5 = 6{,}785 \text{ lb-ft}$$
$$M_G = 6{,}785 + (2{,}215)5 - (2{,}643)5 = 4{,}655 \text{ lb-ft}$$
$$M_H = 4{,}655 + (1{,}785)5 - (1{,}785)5 = 4{,}655 \text{ lb-ft}$$
$$M_J = 4{,}655 + (2{,}643)5 - (2{,}215)5 = 6{,}785 \text{ lb-ft}$$

PROBLEMS

7-9. Calculate the moments at the supports, the reactions, and the maximum positive moments for a 60-ft long beam with four equal spans carrying a load of 3,000 lb concentrated at the mid-point of each span.

7-10. A beam 35 ft long has three equal spans of 10 ft each and an overhang of 5 ft at the right end. It carries a load of 100 lb per linear ft. Calculate the moment at each support, the four reactions, and the moments at the other danger sections.

7-11. A beam 50 ft long has two equal spans of 20 ft each and a span of 10 ft at the right end. It carries loads of 400 lb per ft over the two end spans and a load of 200 lb per ft over the center span. Compute the moment at each support, the reactions, and the positive moments at the other danger sections.

7-12. Figure 7-11 shows a continuous beam with two concentrated loads. Calculate the moment and reaction at each support. Compute the moment at each load.

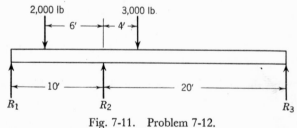

Fig. 7-11. Problem 7-12.

8: Composite Beams

8-1. Introduction

In deriving the flexure formula, $M = sI/c$, it was assumed that the material of the beam was homogeneous (one material) and that the unit stresses varied directly as the distances from the neutral axis. Therefore, this formula does not apply directly to composite (two-material) beams. However, the formula may be used by transforming the section of such a beam to an equivalent section of a homogeneous beam.

The most common types of combination beams are those of steel and wood and of steel and concrete. The modulus of elasticity of steel is 30,000,000 psi, of wood 1,500,000 psi, and of concrete 2,000,000 psi, so that the unit stress in steel for any given unit deformation is 20 times that in wood and 15 times that in concrete. In other words, the same unit deformation will be produced by unit stresses which are proportional to the moduli of elasticity of the two materials. Expressed mathematically, $\epsilon = s_1/E_1 = s_2/E_2$, or in equivalent terms, $s = \epsilon E$.

8-2. Equivalent Beam Sections

Since the stresses at any distance from the neutral axis vary directly as the product of the unit deformation and the modulus of elasticity, it is possible to substitute a beam of homogeneous material for one of two or more materials.

Figure 8-1*a* represents a composite beam of steel and wood. Figure 8-1*b* shows an all-wood section equivalent to the composite wood and steel beam of *a*, and Fig. 8-1*c* shows an all-steel equivalent section. From Art. 8-1 it is apparent that

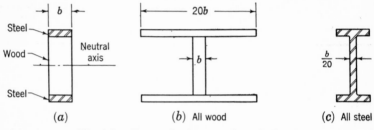

Fig. 8-1. Composite beam and equivalents.

an equivalent wood section would necessarily be 20 times the breadth of the steel, since their moduli of elasticity vary in the ratio of 30,000,000/1,500,000 = 20. Similarly, the breadth of a steel section in place of the wooden part would be $b/20$ in order to maintain the same relation to the neutral axis.

Once the form of the equivalent beam has been determined, the theory of homogeneous beams may be applied as before and any desired information computed.

Example 8-1. A simple timber beam 4 in. wide by 12 in. deep by 12 ft long has a $\frac{1}{4}$- by 4-in. steel strap top and bottom. Calculate the maximum flexural stresses developed in the wood and in the steel by an 8,000-lb load at its mid-point.

SOLUTION: Using E_s = 30,000,000 psi and E_w = 1,500,000 psi,

$$\frac{E_s}{E_w} = \frac{30,000,000}{1,500,000} = 20$$

Figure 8-2*a* shows the actual section, Fig. 8-2*b* the wood equivalent, and Fig. 8-2*c* the steel equivalent. By using the all-wood beam,

$$I_c = \frac{(80)(12.5)^3}{12} - \frac{(76)(12)^3}{12} = 2,100 \text{ in.}^4$$

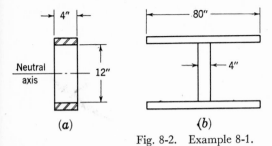
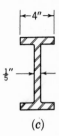

(a) (b) (c)

Fig. 8-2. Example 8-1.

Maximum bending moment:

$$M = \frac{Pl}{4} = \frac{(8,000)(12)(12)}{4} = 288,000 \text{ lb-in.}$$

The flexure formula:

$$\frac{M}{s} = \frac{I}{c}$$

where $c = 6$ in. for maximum fiber stress of wood

$c = 6.25$ in. for maximum fiber stress of steel

Substituting and solving for s,

$$s = \frac{(288,000)6}{2,100} = 820 \text{ psi} \quad \text{for wood}$$

$$s = \frac{(288,000)(6.25)}{2,100} = 860 \text{ psi} \quad \text{for steel}$$

Therefore, the maximum stress in the wood is 820 psi. The maximum stress in the steel is

$$(860)(20) = 17,200 \text{ psi}$$

The problem may also be solved using the all-steel section:

$$I_c = \frac{4(12.5)^3}{12} - \frac{(3.8)12)^3}{12} = 105 \text{ in.}^4$$

The flexure formula, solving for s:

$$s = \frac{Mc}{I} = \frac{(228,000)(6.25)}{105} = 17,200 \text{ psi} \quad \text{for steel}$$

$$s = \frac{(288,000)6}{105} = 1,650 \text{ psi} \quad \text{for wood}$$

Therefore, the maximum stress in steel is 17,200 psi, and the maximum fiber stress in wood is $1,650/20 = 820$ psi, as before.

PROBLEMS

In the following problems, use $E_s = 30,000,000$ psi and

$$E_w = 1,500,000 \text{ psi}$$

8-1. A simple wooden beam 6 in. wide by 12 in. deep by 20 ft long is reinforced with steel plates, 6 in. wide by $\frac{3}{8}$ in. thick, top and bottom. Calculate the maximum fiber stress in each material due to a uniformly distributed load of 500 lb per ft.

8-2. A wooden cantilever beam 8 in. wide by 16 in. deep by 6 ft long is reinforced with steel plates 3 in. wide by $\frac{1}{4}$ in. thick, top and bottom. If $s_s = 18,000$ psi and $s_w = 1,000$ psi, what total load may be safely concentrated at its free end?

8-3. A simple wooden beam 6 in. wide by 14 in. deep by 18 ft long is to carry a load of 5,000 lb concentrated at its mid-point. The beam is to be reinforced with steel plates 6 in. wide. Calculate the thickness required. Assume $s_w = 1,000$ psi.

8-4. A wooden cantilever beam 6 in. wide by 10 in. deep with a free length of 8 ft reinforced with steel plates 6 in. wide supports a uniformly distributed load of 500 lb per ft. Calculate the thickness of plates required. Assume $s_w = 1,000$ psi.

8-5. Calculate the maximum fiber stress in each material of a composite cantilever beam made up of a 6- by 6-in. wooden beam reinforced with 6- by $\frac{1}{4}$-in. steel plates, top and bottom. The beam is 6 ft long and supports a uniformly distributed load of 100 lb per ft and a load of 1,000 lb concentrated at its free end.

8-3. Reinforced-concrete Beams

Concrete is relatively weak in tension and strong in compression. Thus concrete beams are reinforced with steel rods imbedded near the surface of the tension side of the beam in order to resist the tensile stress and to utilize the high compressive strength of concrete.

Two factors make such a nonhomogeneous combination possible: they have approximately the same coefficients of expansion, thus expanding and contracting at very similar rates for the same temperature change; and there is a strong bond between concrete and steel, so that to bend the concrete, the steel must also bend. This bond can be increased by mechanical devices such as roughening the surface of the steel rods or twisting or bending them into various shapes.

8-4. Notation

The following notations will be used for reinforced-concrete. In large part, they agree with notations previously used. Figure 8-3 shows in part the notation used on reinforced-concrete beams.

s_s = unit fiber stress in steel

s_c = unit fiber stress in concrete

e_s = unit deformation (elongation) in steel

e_c = unit deformation (contraction) in outer fiber of concrete

E_s = modulus of elasticity of steel, 30,000,000 psi

E_c = modulus of elasticity of concrete, 2,000,000 psi

$$n = \frac{E_s}{E_c} = \frac{30,000,000}{2,000,000} = 15$$

T = total tension in steel at section of beam

C = total compression in concrete at same section

b = breadth (or width) of rectangular beam

d = distance from outermost compressive fibers to plane of steel

p = percentage of steel reinforcement (ratio of steel area A to concrete area $bd = A/bd$)

K = ratio of depth of neutral axis of section below top to d

A = area of cross section of steel

M_s = resisting moment as determined by steel

M_c = resisting moment as determined by concrete

M = resisting moment in general

j = ratio of the arm of resisting couple to d

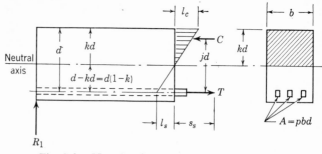

Fig. 8-3. Notation for reinforced-concrete beams.

8-5. Methods of Solution

There are two general methods of solution.

The first method is an adaptation of the equivalent beam method used on composite beams of steel and wood. In this method the computation becomes a rather laborious task because of the unsymmetrical shape of the equivalent all-concrete or all-steel beam.

The second method, therefore, is the one most generally used. The internal resisting moment is expressed in terms of the resultant tensile or compressive force acting at any section and the distance between these resultant forces.

By similar triangles, the unit deformation at the center of the reinforcement is to the unit deformation in the outer fibers of the concrete as the distance from the neutral axis to the center of the reinforcement is to the distance from the neutral axis to the outer fibers of the concrete. Thus

$$\frac{e_s}{e_c} = \frac{d(1 - K)}{Kd} = \frac{1 - K}{K}$$

Since the modulus of elasticity (E) is a ratio of the unit stress to unit strain, provided the elastic limit is not exceeded,

$$e_s = \frac{S_s}{E_s} \quad \text{and} \quad e_c = \frac{s_c}{E_c}$$

from which

$$\frac{e_s}{e_c} = \frac{s_s}{E_s} \times \frac{E_c}{s_c}$$

but the modulus of elasticity of steel is n times that of concrete:

$$E_s = nE_c$$

Substituting,

$$\frac{e_s}{e_c} = \frac{s_s}{ns_c} = \frac{1 - K}{K}$$

and

$$s_s = \frac{ns_c(1 - K)}{K}$$

The area of the concrete in compression in a rectangular section is bkd and the average unit stress over this area is $s_c/2$. Therefore, total compressive stress is

$$C = \frac{s_c}{2} bkd$$

and total tensile stress in steel is

$$T = A_s ns_c \frac{(1 - K)}{K}$$

since the percentage of steel reinforcement is $p = A_s/bd$, or $A_s = pbd$.

The steel is considered to resist all the tensile stress, and so the concrete below the neutral axis does not take any of the tensile stress. Therefore the total tension in the steel equals the total compression in the concrete, or

$$C = T$$
$$\frac{s_c}{2} bkd = pbdns_c \frac{(1 - K)}{K}$$
$$k^2 = 2Pn(1 - k)$$
$$k^2 = 2Pn - 2Pnk$$
$$k^2 + 2Pnk - 2pn = 0$$
$$k = \sqrt{2pn + (pn)^2} - pn$$

If p and n are known or assumed, the value of K can be determined. Since d is the distance from the outermost compressive fibers to the plane of the steel and Kd is the distance from the outermost compressive fibers to the neutral axis, the position of the neutral surface is known when the value of K is determined.

The total tension T may also be expressed as the product of the area of steel and the unit stress in steel:

$$T = A_s s_s$$

And the total compression C may be expressed as the product of the area in compression and unit stress of concrete:

$$C = bkd \frac{(s_c)}{2}$$

Also, from equilibrium, the internal resisting moment must equal the external bending moment: $M_R = M$.

The internal resisting moment is the moment of the couple formed by the total compressive stress C and the total tensile stress T. This moment is $C \times jd$ (or $T \times jd$).

Since the action line of C is at a distance $Kd/3$ (see Fig. 5-2, Art. 5-1) from the top surface of the beam,

$$jd = d - \frac{Kd}{3}$$

$$j = 1 - \frac{K}{3}$$

Substituting the value of T and noting that $A_s = pbd$, the equation $M = M_R$ becomes

$$M = Tjd = A_s s_s jd = pjbd^2 s_s$$

or

$$s_s = \frac{M}{pjbd^2}$$

Similarly

$$s_c = \frac{2M}{Kjbd^2}$$

Example 8-2. A reinforced-concrete beam with a span of 20 ft is 10 in. wide by 17.5 in. deep. It has six ⅝-in.-diam steel rods placed with their centers 16 in. from the top. Calculate the maximum unit stresses developed in each material because of a 5,000-lb load concentrated at the mid-point of the span.

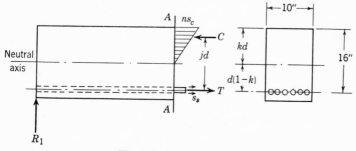

Fig. 8-4. Example 8-2.

SOLUTION: From Fig. 8-4

$$A_s = 6\pi r^2 = 6(3.142)(\tfrac{5}{16})^2 = 1.84 \text{ sq in.}$$

$$p = \frac{A_s}{bd} = \frac{1.84}{(10)(16)} = 0.012$$

$$K = \sqrt{2pn + (pn)^2} - pn$$
$$= \sqrt{2(0.012)15 + (0.012 \times 15)^2} - (0.012)15$$
$$K = 0.446$$

$$Kd = (0.446)16 = 7.14 \text{ in.}$$

$$j = 1 - \frac{K}{3} = 1 - \frac{0.446}{3} = 0.851$$

$$jd = (0.851)16 = 13.6 \text{ in.}$$

$$M = \frac{Pl}{4} = \frac{(5,000)(20)(12)}{4} = 300,000 \text{ lb-in.}$$

$$s_c = \frac{2M}{Kjbd^2} = \frac{(2)(300,000)}{(0.446)(13.6)(10)(16)} = 620 \text{ psi} \quad \text{(compression)}$$

$$s_s = \frac{M}{pjdb^2} = \frac{300,000}{(0.012)(13.6)(10)(16)} = 11,540 \text{ psi} \quad \text{(tension)}$$

PROBLEMS

8-6. A reinforced-concrete beam supported at the ends is 18 ft long and 6 in. wide by $13\frac{1}{2}$ in. deep. It has four $\frac{1}{2}$-in.-diam steel rods which are placed with their centers 12 in. from the top. Calculate the maximum unit stress in each material due to a uniformly distributed load of 200 lb per linear ft.

8-7. A reinforced-concrete beam supported at the ends is 20 ft long and 12 in. wide by 16 in. deep and has eight $\frac{1}{2}$-in. steel rods placed with their centers $14\frac{1}{2}$ in. from the top. Assuming maximum allowable unit stresses of 850 psi for concrete and 18,000 psi for steel, what total uniformly distributed load, including the weight of the beam, can it carry?

8-8. A simple beam of reinforced concrete has a span of 24 ft and is 6 in. wide by 20 in. deep. It has four $\frac{3}{4}$-in.-diam steel rods placed with their centers 18 in. from the top. Calculate the maximum unit stresses in each material if a 4,000-lb load is placed at the center of the span.

8-9. A reinforced-concrete beam 14 in. wide by 24 in. deep and 40 ft long is supported at the ends and at the middle. It has eight $\frac{3}{4}$-in. steel rods placed 22 in. from the top of the beam. What total uniformly distributed load, including the weight of the beam, can it carry?

8-10. If concrete weighs 150 lb per cu ft, what total load may be placed midway between the supports in Prob. 8-9?

8-11. Calculate the necessary cross-sectional area of steel rods for a reinforced-concrete beam 12 in. wide by 16 in. deep with a span of 24 ft. The rods are to be placed 14 in. from the top, and there will be a load of 5,000 lb placed at the center of the span.

8-6. Balanced Reinforcement

The ideal and most economical design of reinforced-concrete beams requires that both materials should be stressed to the allowable limit. This maximum stress in both materials will be attained only when $p = As/bd$ has a definite value. Since at any section, $C = T$,

$$\frac{s_c Kbd}{2} = s_s pbd$$

$$p = \frac{s_c K}{2s_s}$$

which may be written

$$p = \frac{K}{2s_s/s_c}$$

Also, since the stresses vary directly as the distances from the neutral axis,

$$\frac{ns_c}{s_s} = \frac{Kd}{(1 - K)d} = \frac{K}{1 - K}$$

Solving for K,

$$K = \frac{ns_c}{s_s + ns_c}$$

Substituting in the equation for p gives

$$p = \frac{1}{(2s_s/s_c)(s_s/ns_c + 1)}$$

The allowable stresses s_c and s_s are usually specified by the building code. The value of n is the ratio of the moduli of elasticity, E_s/E_c. Consequently, p may be determined directly from the preceding equation.

8-7. Design of Reinforced-concrete Beams

The following procedure may be used in the design of reinforced-concrete beams:

1. The safe unit stresses for steel and concrete are usually known in any design problem. For simplicity in the following problems, they shall be $s_s = 18,000$ psi and $s_c = 800$ psi.

2. The value of n is

$$\frac{E_s}{E_c} = \frac{30,000,000}{2,000,000} = 15$$

3. Determine K from the formula

$$\frac{ns_c}{s_s} = \frac{K}{1 - K}$$

4. Determine j from the formula

$$j = 1 - \frac{K}{3}$$

5. For balanced reinforcement, determine p from the formula

$$p = \frac{1}{(2s_s/s_c)(s_s/ns_c + 1)}$$

6. Calculate maximum bending moment.

7. Substituting in the formula $s_c = 2M/Kjbd^2$, a solution is made for bd^2. The relationship between b and d either is specified by the conditions of the problem or arbitrarily determined.

8. With b and d established, the area of the steel is given by the equation $As = pbd$.

The required steel area may be supplied by any conveniently sized rods. The most commonly used sizes are ½-, ⅝-, and ¾-in.-diam rods. It is customary to allow 1½ in. of concrete below the rods to secure a satisfactory bond between the concrete and the steel.

Example 8-3. Design a reinforced-concrete beam with balanced reinforcement for a 12-ft span to withstand a uniformly distributed load of 1,000 lb per ft when $d = 2b$

SOLUTION:

1. Solving for K,

$$\frac{ns_c}{s_s} = \frac{K}{1 - K}$$
$$\frac{(15)(800)}{18,000} = \frac{K}{1 - K}$$
$$K = 0.4$$

2. Solving for j,

$$j = 1 - \frac{K}{3} = 1 - \frac{0.4}{3} = 0.889$$

3. Solving for p,

$$p = \frac{1}{(2s_s/s_c)(s_s/ns_c + 1)} = \frac{1}{(2 \times 18{,}000/800)(18{,}000/15 \times 800 + 1)}$$
$$= 0.009$$

4. Maximum bending moment:

$$M = \frac{Wl}{8} = \frac{(12{,}000)(12)(12)}{8} = 216{,}000 \text{ lb-in.}$$

5. Solving for bd,

$$s_c = \frac{2M}{Kjbd^2}$$

$$800 = \frac{2 \times 216{,}000}{(0.4)(0.889)(bd^2)}$$
$$bd^2 = 1{,}520$$

Since $d = 2b$,

$$b^3 = 380$$
$$b = 7.25 \text{ in., or } 8 \text{ in.}$$
$$d = 16 \text{ in.}$$

6. Area of steel:

$$As = pbd = (0.009)(8)(16) = 1.15 \text{ in.}$$

7. Assuming $\frac{1}{2}$-in.-diam steel rods and calculating the number required,

$$n = \frac{A}{\pi r^2} = \frac{1.15}{(3.14)(\frac{1}{4})^2} = 5.9 \qquad \text{Use 6.}$$

PROBLEMS

8-12. Design a reinforced-concrete beam with balanced reinforcement for a 16-ft span to carry a uniformly distributed load of 800 lb per ft including its own weight and a load of 2,000 lb concentrated at its mid-point. The depth of the beam is twice its breadth.

8-13. Design a reinforced-concrete beam with balanced reinforcement which is 16 ft long between fixed ends. The beam is to carry a uniform load of 1,000 lb per ft including its own weight.

8-14. A balanced reinforced-concrete beam is 10 in. wide and carries a load of 12,000 lb concentrated at the mid-point of its 12-ft span.   Calculate the depth of beam required and the number of $\frac{5}{8}$-in.-diam steel rods necessary.   Concrete weighs 150 lb per cu ft.

8-15. Design a reinforced-concrete beam with balanced reinforcement for a span of 14 ft carrying a uniformly distributed load of 1,200 lb per ft not including its own weight and $d = 2b$.   Concrete weighs 150 lb per cu ft.

8-16. Calculate the maximum uniformly distributed load which a reinforced-concrete beam 10 in. wide by 18 in. deep may carry over its span of 10 ft if it has five $\frac{3}{4}$-in.-diam steel rods placed 16 in. from the top for reinforcement.

8-17. In Prob. 8-13 calculate the size of a beam required if it is to be square.   Which would be the preferred design?

8-18. Design a continuous reinforced-concrete beam with balanced reinforcement which has three spans of 20 ft each and carries a uniformly distributed load of 1,200 lb per ft including its own weight.   Assume $d = 2b$.

$9:$ Columns

9-1. Introduction

One of the most controversial subjects in the engineering field has to do with the design of columns. An incredible number of column formulas has been developed by various qualified and unqualified persons, and the AISC saw fit to print as many as 28 formulas for structural steel alone in their 1928 Handbook. Progress has been made in recent years in the direction of simplification and standardization, and it is not too much to expect even greater progress in the very near future. However, because of the great variety of materials used in columns and various other factors which affect the strength of columns, such as end conditions and the length of columns relative to their cross-sectional dimensions, there will always be a considerable number of formulas from which to select. The problem of selection of the proper formula, however, is not a serious one, since in actual practice the particular column formula to use in any given problem is generally fixed by the various qualified agencies, such as the AISC and the building codes.

Therefore, it will not be the purpose of this chapter to make a comprehensive study of column formulas, but to present the basic principles of column theory.

9-2. Compression Members

A compression member is a solid or built-up bar which is subjected to compressive loads at the ends acting parallel to the axis of the bar. Compression members are generally separated into three classes:

1. Short posts or compression blocks.
2. Intermediate columns.
3. Long columns.

A short post is a compression member which has a cross-sectional area sufficiently large with respect to its length that, when a load is applied at the centroid of its cross section, the post will fail by crushing or yielding of its material. Thus, the strength of a short post is limited by the strength of its material, and the load it may carry is determined by the formula $P = As$.

A long column is a compression member whose cross-sectional area with respect to its length is such that a load applied at its ends will cause the column to bend or buckle rather than to crush or yield. Thus, the strength of a column is not limited by the strength of its material, and the long column exceeds the specifications as expressed by the formula $P = As$, thereby requiring other formulas for the calculation of safe loads.

Between the short post and the long column are the intermediate columns whose proportions are such that they have some of the characteristics of both the short post and the long column. Most of the columns used in ordinary structure belong to the intermediate-column class.

The factors which most affect the strength of columns are (1) slenderness ratio, (2) end conditions, (3) material, and (4) initial eccentricity of load.

The materials most widely used for columns are structural steel, wrought iron, cast iron, and timber.

Even though the load may be applied at the centroid of the column, lack of straightness and presence of defects in the material of a column will produce an eccentricity between the action line of the load and the centroid of the stress-resisting portion at one or more cross sections.

9-3. Radius of Gyration

In Chap. 4 the moment of inertia of an area was defined to be the sum of the products of the elemental areas, each multiplied by the square of its distance from the reference axis to its centroid. Expressed in equation form, $I = Ad^2$. If we let d equal some constant distance K at which the entire area could be considered as being concentrated without changing its moment of inertia, then $I = AK^2$ or $K = \sqrt{I/A}$, the radius of gyration. A compression member tends to buckle or bend in the direction of its least radius of gyration. Thus, in Fig. 9-1, the column will tend to bend about the Y-Y axis rather than the X-X axis because the radius of gyration with respect to the Y-Y axis is less than it is with respect to the X-X axis.

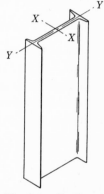

Fig. 9-1. Radius of gyration.

Radii of gyration of all standard sections and many built-up combination sections may be found in handbooks under the section entitled "Properties of Sections."

Since the radii of gyration are functions of a column cross section, they serve as measures of a column's lateral stability. Space and directional strength requirements permitting, the radii of gyration are made as nearly alike as possible, so that the column will be equally strong in either direction and will not carry an uneconomical and unnecessary amount of material.

9-4. Slenderness Ratio

The strength of a column free to bend laterally in any direction decreases as the ratio of its unsupported length to its least radius of gyration increases. This ratio (l/K) is called the *slenderness* ratio for columns.

The limiting ranges in slenderness ratio for the three types of compression members *when made of steel* are about as follows:

1. Short posts: $l/K > 0 < 60$.
2. Intermediate columns: $l/K > 60 < 150$.
3. Long columns: $l/K > 150$.

9-5. End Arrangements

The amount of restraint imposed at the ends of a column is a very important factor in determining its strength. Theoretically, the limits of restraint are found in fixed ends and free ends. Between these limits lie the end arrangements found in structures and machines.

Fixed ends are held rigidly so that the direction of the column axis remains constant under all loads.

Free ends allow freedom to turn but not to move laterally. Columns with this type of end condition are called *round-*, *pivot-*, or *hinge-ended*.

Quite often, combinations are encountered with one end fixed and the other end free to turn but not free to move laterally when the column bends.

Figure 9-2 shows the effect of various end conditions on tall slender columns. When a load is applied to a column with fixed ends (Fig. 9-2*a*), it causes the column to bend in such a manner that the inflection points are at the quarter-points of the unsupported length of the column. Since inflection points are points of zero bending moment, they are also points equivalent to the ends of a column with both ends hinged (Fig. 9-2*c*). Thus, the middle half of the unsupported length of a fixed-ended column may be considered as equivalent to a hinge-ended column.

A column with one end fixed and the other end hinged to allow freedom to rotate but not to move laterally (Fig. 9-2*b*) will have its inflection point approximately 0.7*l* from the hinged end of the column.

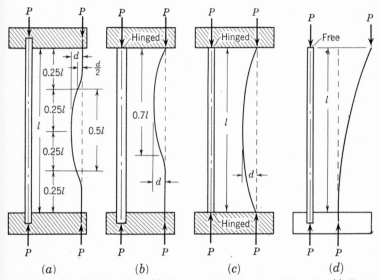

Fig. 9-2. (*a*) Fixed ends. (*b*) One end fixed, other hinged. (*c*) Both ends hinged. (*d*) One end fixed, other end free.

A column with one end fixed and the other end wholly free to move laterally as well as to rotate (Fig. 9-2*d*), would have to be rotated its full length about its base to make a column similar to one with both ends hinged. Its equivalent length, therefore, is equal to 2*l*.

It can be shown that the load-carrying capacity of a column increases in inverse proportion to the square of the distance between the inflection points. Thus, a column with fixed ends is four times as strong as one with hinged ends; a column with one end fixed and the other hinged is twice as strong; a column with one end fixed and the other end free is only one-fourth as strong.

Table 9-1

END CONDITION	EFFECTIVE LENGTH	NUMBER OF TIMES STRONGER THAN HINGED COLUMN
Both ends fixed	$0.5l$	4
One end fixed, other hinged	$0.7l$	2
Both ends hinged	$1.0l$	1
One end fixed, other free	$2.0l$	¼

9-6. Rankine's Formulas

Among the various formulas used for the design of columns, the Rankine formula is one of the most widely used for calculating the strength of steel and iron columns of any length. It states

$$\frac{P}{A} = \frac{s_u}{1 + q(l/K)^2}$$

where P = safe load, lb

A = cross-sectional area, sq in.

s_u = ultimate strength of very short post, psi.

l = length of column, in.

K = least radius of gyration, in.

q = constant dependent on end conditions and material

Rankine suggested empirical values of s and q derived from tests. For structural steel and wrought iron he suggested $s = 36,000$ psi with $q = 1/36,000$ for fixed ends, $q = 1/9,000$ for free ends, and $q = 1/18,000$ for one end fixed and one end free. If a factor of safety of 2 is used, the Rankine formula becomes

$$\frac{P}{A} = \frac{18,000}{1 + q(l/K)^2}$$

9-7. AISC Formulas for Steel Columns

The American Institute of Steel Construction in its 1952 Handbook suggests the following formulas for steel columns:

1. Main or secondary members with values of $l/K \gtreqless 60$ $\gtreqless 120$:

$$\frac{P}{A} = 17,000 - 0.485 \left(\frac{l}{K}\right)^2$$

2. Bracing and secondary members with values of $l/K \gtreqless 120 \gtreqless 200$:

$$\frac{P}{A} = \frac{18,000}{1 + (1/18,000)(l/K)^2}$$

3. Main members with values of $l/K \gtreqless 120 \leq 200$:

$$\frac{P}{A} = \left[\frac{18,000}{1 + (1/18,000)(l/K)^2}\right]\left(1.6 - \frac{l/K}{200}\right)$$

For ratios of l/K less than 60, the compression member is classified as a short post and the load it may carry is limited by the strength of its material so that the formula $P = As$ applies.

9-8. Investigation of Columns

The investigation of the load-carrying capacity of compression members involves the following steps:

1. Determination of the least radius of gyration.
2. Computation of the slenderness ratio l/K and the classification of the member as (*a*) short post, (*b*) intermediate column, or (*c*) long column.
3. Computation of the allowable load according to the formula specified for the particular class of compression member.

Example 9-1.   Determine the safe load which can be carried by a hollow structural-steel column 8 in. square with ½-in. thick walls and 16 ft long using AISC specifications.

SOLUTION:

$$A = 8^2 - 7^2 = 64 - 49 = 15 \text{ sq in.}$$
$$l = (16)12 = 192 \text{ in.}$$
$$I = \frac{bh^3}{12} - \frac{b_1 h_1^3}{12} = \frac{8^4}{12} - \frac{7^4}{12} = 140 \text{ in.}^4$$
$$K = \sqrt{\frac{I}{A}} = \sqrt{\frac{140}{15}} = 3.06 \text{ in.}$$
$$\frac{l}{K} = \frac{192}{3.06} = 63$$

Therefore $P/A = 17,000 - 0.485(l/K)^2$ applies:

$$\frac{P}{A} = 17,000 - 0.485(63)^2$$
$$\frac{P}{A} = 17,000 - 1,920 = 15,080 \text{ psi}$$
$$P = (15,080)15 = 226,000 \text{ lb}$$

In the AISC Handbook, a table of allowable unit stresses is given on pp. 209–210 (1952 edition). This table simplifies the computational work considerably.

Having determined the l/K ratio to be 63, we read across this figure 15.08. This is the allowable unit stress in kips per sq in. (1 kip = 1,000 lb).

Then $(15.08)1,000 = 15,080$ psi as before.

Example 9-2.   Determine the safe load for a 10 I 35 American Standard section when used as a column 4 ft long and as a bracing column 15 ft long, using AISC specifications.

SOLUTION: From the tables, $A = 10.22$ sq in.; least $K = 0.91$ in. For the 4-ft length,

$$\frac{l}{K} = \frac{(12) \times 4}{0.91} = 52.8$$

Therefore, this member is a short post and $P = As$ applies.

$$P = (10.22)(35,000) = 358,000 \text{ lb} \qquad \text{ANS.}$$

For the 15-ft length,

$$\frac{l}{K} = \frac{(12) \times 15}{0.91} = 198$$

Therefore, this member is a long column:

$$\frac{P}{A} = \frac{18,000}{1 + (1/18,000)(l/K)^2}$$

$$\frac{P}{A} = \frac{(18,000)}{1 + (1/18,000)(39,200)} = 5,660 \text{ psi} \qquad \text{ANS.}$$

In the table on p. 210 of the Handbook, an l/K ratio of 198 for secondary members gives an allowable stress of $(5.66)1,000 = 5,660$ psi.

If this column were to be used as a main member, the allowable unit stress would be $(3.45)1,000 = 3,450$ psi. With a cross-sectional area of 10.22 sq in., the total permissible load is 35,000 lb as compared with 57,000 lb as a secondary member.

PROBLEMS

9-1. Calculate the safe load which may be applied to a 10-in. square hollow steel column 20 ft long and with 1-in. walls, using AISC specifications.

9-2. What safe load may be applied to a 10-in.-diam hollow steel column with 1-in. walls 20 ft long according to AISC specifications?

9-3. Determine the safe axial load which may be carried by a 10 WF 45 American Standard structural-steel shape when used as columns 6, 12, and 24 ft long.

9-4. Calculate the safe load on a 12 WF 72 American Standard structural-steel column 12 ft long which is to have both ends fixed, using the Rankine formula.

9-5. Determine the maximum length a column 8 in. square may have to be classified as a short post. Calculate the maximum allowable load which may be applied.

9-6. What maximum length may the column of Prob. 9-5 have if it is to be used as a main compression member? Calculate the maximum allowable load using AISC specifications.

9-7. If the column in Prob. 9-5 is to be used as a secondary compression member, what maximum length may it have and what allowable load can it carry, using AISC specifications?

9-9. Design of Columns

The design or selection of a column generally consists in determining the required cross-sectional dimensions, having the length and load predetermined by the conditions of the problem.

When the cross section has one unknown dimension, such as a square, a circle, or a rectangle with fixed relationship between the sides, the design consists in solving a specified column formula for the single unknown.

If the cross section is built up from structural-steel shapes, etc., there will be more than one unknown, and the problem becomes one of selection by trial.

Example 9-3. Determine the size of a square structural-steel column 8 ft long which will be required to carry an axial load of 100,000 lb, using AISC specifications.

SOLUTION: Let a = side of square:

$$I = \frac{a^4}{12} \quad \text{and} \quad K^2 = \frac{I}{A} = \frac{a^4/12}{a^2} = \frac{a^2}{12}$$

Using the formula for main columns,

$$\frac{P}{A} = 17{,}000 - 0.485 \left(\frac{l}{K}\right)^2$$
$$\frac{100{,}000}{a^2} = 17{,}000 - (0.485) \left(\frac{9{,}216}{a^2/12}\right)$$
$$a^2 = 9.05$$
$$a = 3.01 \text{ in.} \quad \text{ANS.}$$

Checking for the slenderness ratio,

$$K = \sqrt{\frac{a^2}{12}} = \sqrt{\frac{9.05}{12}} = 0.868 \text{ in.}$$
$$\frac{l}{K} = \frac{96}{0.868} = 110.5$$

Since the ratio is within the limits for main columns, the solution is valid.

Example 9-4.   Select an I beam to be used as a column 16 ft long carrying a load of 200,000 lb.   Use AISC specifications.

SOLUTION: The minimum possible cross-sectional area for a short post is

$$A = \frac{P}{s} = \frac{200,000}{18,000} = 11.11 \text{ sq in.}$$

Since a column will require considerably more area, try a 15 I 70 section.   From the tables, $A = 20.38$ sq in.; least $K = 1.19$ in. Since

$$\frac{l}{K} = \frac{192}{1.19} = 161.5$$

use

$$\frac{P}{A} = \frac{18,000}{1 + (1/18,000)(l/K)^2} = \frac{18,000}{1 + 26,082/18,000} = 7,350 \text{ psi}$$

but

$$\frac{P}{A} = \frac{200,000}{20.38} = 9,800 \text{ psi}$$

Therefore 9,800 > 7,350

The left side of the foregoing inequality is the average unit load, and the right side is the allowable unit load.   Since the allowable unit load is considerably less than the average unit load, it is evident that a heavier section must be used.

Trying a 20 I 90 section, from the tables, $A = 26.26$ sq in.; least $K = 1.36$ in.
Since

$$\frac{l}{K} = \frac{192}{1.36} = 141$$

use

$$\frac{P}{A} = \frac{18,000}{1 + (1/18,000)(l/K)^2} = \frac{18,000}{1 + 19,900/18,000} = 8,600 \text{ psi}$$

but

$$\frac{P}{A} = \frac{200,000}{26.26} = 7,600$$

Therefore $7,600 < 8,600$ and this section is too large. Trying a 20 I 81.4 section, from the tables, $A = 23.74$ sq in.; least $K = 1.39$ in.

$$\frac{l}{K} = \frac{192}{1.39} = 138$$

$$\frac{P}{A} = \frac{18,000}{1 + (1/18,000)(l/K)^2} = \frac{18,000}{1 + 19,044/18,000} = 8,750 \text{ psi}$$

and

$$\frac{P}{A} = \frac{200,000}{23.74} = 8,420 \text{ psi}$$

Therefore $8,420 < 8,750$

The average unit load is less than the allowable unit load, so this section is satisfactory in strength.

It will carry a total load $P = (23.74)(8,750) = 208,000$ lb, which is more than the required amount.

PROBLEMS

9-8. Calculate the diameter of a round structural-steel column 24 ft long to carry a load of 300,000 lb, using AISC specifications.

9-9. Determine the dimensions of a rectangular steel column 10 ft long which is to carry a load of 250,000 lb. The section is to have one side twice the other. Use AISC specifications.

9-10. Calculate the cross-sectional dimensions of a hollow circular structural-steel column 16 ft long to carry a load of 500,000 lb using AISC specifications.

9-11. Select the lightest WF column 15 ft long to carry 150,000 lb according to AISC specifications.

9-12. Select the lightest WF column 26 ft long to carry a load of 1,000,000 lb, using AISC specifications.

9-13. Select the lightest I beam to be used as a column 12 ft long carrying a load of 100,000 lb. Use AISC specifications.

9-14. Two channels are to be placed together back to back to form a column 20 ft long. Determine the lightest channels which will support 500,000 lb, using AISC specifications.

9-10. Other Column Formulas

As stated in Art. 9-1, countless column formulas have appeared from time to time, each with its own specifications and limitations.

A few of the more commonly used formulas are those developed by the New York and Chicago building codes for cast iron and structural steel, the Aluminum Co. of America (Alcoa) for aluminum, and the U.S. Department of Agriculture Forest Products Laboratory for wood.

These formulas will now be stated with the slenderness ratio for which they apply.

New York building code: Cast-iron columns:

$$\frac{P}{A} = 9{,}000 - 40\frac{l}{K} \qquad \text{when } \frac{l}{K} < 70$$

Chicago building code: Steel columns:
Main members:

$$\frac{P}{A} = 16{,}000 - 70\frac{l}{K} \qquad \text{when } \frac{l}{K} = 30 < 120$$

Secondary members:

$$\frac{P}{A} = 16{,}000 - 70\frac{l}{K} \qquad \text{when } \frac{l}{K} = 30 < 150$$

Alcoa formula: Aluminum columns:

$$\frac{P}{A} = 15{,}000 - 123\frac{l}{K} \qquad \text{when } \frac{l}{K} < 81$$

$$\frac{P}{A} = \frac{33{,}000{,}000}{(l/K)^2} \qquad \text{when } \frac{l}{K} > 81$$

U.S. Department of Agriculture: Wood columns:
In the following formulas,

s = allowable compressive stress parallel to grain for specific kind of wood

d = least dimension of cross section of column

K = constant derived from formula $(\pi/2)\ \sqrt{E/6s}$

$$P = As \qquad\qquad\qquad\qquad \text{when } \frac{l}{d} < 11$$

$$\frac{P}{A} = s\left[1 - \frac{1}{3}\left(\frac{l}{Kd}\right)^4\right] \qquad \text{when } \frac{l}{d} = 11 \text{ to } < K$$

$$\frac{P}{A} = \frac{\pi^2 E}{36(l/d)^2} \qquad\qquad \text{when } \frac{l}{d} > K < 50$$

These formulas have a factor of safety of 3.

PROBLEMS

9-15. Determine the safe load on a 15 I 50 American Standard beam used as a column 12 ft long, using the Chicago building code formula.

9-16. Calculate the safe load on a 8 WF 40 American Standard beam used as a column 20 ft long using the Chicago building code formula.

9-17. An aluminum compression member 8 in. square has walls 2 in. thick. If it is 18 ft long, what compressive load may it carry according to the Alcoa specifications?

9-18. If the compression member of Prob. 9-9 is made of spruce for which E = 1,200,000 psi and s = 800 psi parallel to the grain, what load may be applied?

9-19. Design a square aluminum column 8 ft long which will carry a compressive load of 160,000 lb, using the Alcoa specifications.

9-20. Select the lightest WF column 15 ft long to carry a load of 150,000 lb, using the Chicago building code formula.

9-21. A column with a hollow rectangular section is made by joining together four 2- by 12-in. spruce planks. What maximum load may be applied to the column if it is 8, 12, and 25 ft long?

10: Torsion

10-1. Torsional Loads and Twisting Moment or Torque

External forces which cause a bar to twist about its central axis are called *torsional loads*. In a bar that is twisted about its own axis, the stress produced is due to shear and is called *torsion*. The fibers on the outer surface take the form of

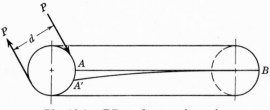

Fig. 10-1. Effect of external couple.

spirals, while the neutral axis remains unaffected. The algebraic sum of the product of the external forces and their distance to the axis of the shaft is called the *twisting moment* or *torque*. The symbol T will be used to denote torque. It is generally expressed in inch-pounds.

In Fig. 10-1, the effect of an external couple Pd is illustrated. Point A has moved to point A' and the straight line AB has become a helix $A'B$. This indicates that the plane circular section at the left end of the shaft has moved clockwise relative to the plane circular section at the right end. This relative movement of the sections is resisted by the material of the shaft, thereby setting up internal resisting moments. For the shaft to be in equilibrium, it must necessarily follow that an internal resisting moment is set up which equals the external twisting moment.

10-2. The Torque Formula

In deriving the flexure formula for beams,

$$M = s \frac{I}{c}$$

where M = bending moment and is equal to the resisting moment M_R

the symbol I = moment of inertia

c = distance from rectangular axis to outermost fibers

It can be shown by higher mathematics that

$$T = s \frac{I}{c}$$

where T = twisting moment

c = distance from center of shaft (pole) to outermost fibers

I = polar moment of inertia

Since I is generally reserved for rectangular moment of inertia, it is customary to use the symbol J to denote the polar moment of inertia.

Thus the torque formula becomes

$$T = s \frac{J}{c}$$

10-3. The Torque Formula for Solid Circular Shafts

Since the distance from the center of a shaft to its outer fiber equals the radius of the shaft, then

$$c = r = \frac{d}{2}$$

The polar moment of inertia of a circle is

$$J = \frac{\pi d^4}{32}$$

By substitution,

$$T = s\frac{\pi d^4/32}{d/2} = s\left(\frac{\pi d^4}{32}\right)\left(\frac{2}{d}\right)$$

Simplifying,

$$T = \frac{\pi s d^3}{16} = 0.196sd^3$$

which is the torque formula for a solid shaft.

PROBLEMS

10-1. Compute the torque required to develop a shearing stress of 10,000 psi on a cylindrical steel shaft 4 in. diam.

10-2. Calculate the diameter of a shaft to carry a torque of 80,000 lb-in. if the maximum shearing stress is not to exceed 8,000 psi.

10-3. What is the maximum shearing stress developed in a shaft 6 in. diam by a torque of 100,000 lb-in.?

10-4. A solid steel shaft $2\frac{1}{4}$ in. diam is twisted by a force of 750 lb applied at a point 2 ft from its axis. Compute the maximum unit shearing stress developed.

10-5. If the ultimate shearing strength of a certain steel is 50,000 psi, at what twisting moment would a 3-in.-diam shaft made of this material fail?

10-6. Determine the diameter of a shaft which is to resist a 1,200-lb load applied 18 in. from its axis. The allowable unit shearing stress is not to exceed 10,000 psi.

10-4. The Torque Formula for Hollow Shafts

Figure 10-2 shows the cross section of a hollow shaft. The polar moment of inertia is

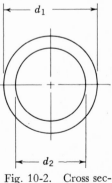

Fig. 10-2. Cross section of hollow shaft.

$$J = \frac{\pi}{32} (d_1{}^4 - d_2{}^4)$$

Substituting in the torque formula,

$$T = \frac{s(\pi/32)(d_1{}^4 - d_2{}^4)}{d_1/2} = \frac{0.196s(d_1{}^4 - d_2{}^4)}{d_1}$$

which is the torque formula for hollow shafts.

PROBLEMS

10-7. Calculate the polar moment of inertia of a hollow circular shaft with 6 in. OD and $4\frac{1}{2}$ in. ID.

10-8. Compute the torque required to develop a shearing stress of 10,000 psi on a hollow steel shaft with an OD of $4\frac{1}{4}$ in. and an ID of $2\frac{1}{2}$ in. Compare with Prob. 10-1.

10-9. A hollow shaft with $3\frac{1}{2}$ in. OD and 2 in. ID is twisted by a force of 750 lb applied at a point 3 ft from its axis. Compute the maximum unit shearing stress developed.

10-5. Angle of Twist of a Cylindrical Shaft

Figure 10-3 represents a shaft fixed at the lower end. *AB* is a line on its surface parallel to the axis. When the shaft is twisted by a force applied at its free end, the straight line *AB* becomes a helix *AB'* turning through the angle θ.

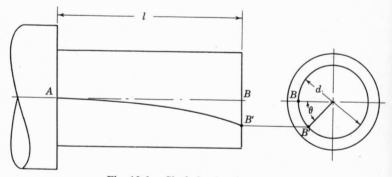

Fig. 10-3. Shaft fixed at lower end.

In some cases, the size of shaft necessary to transmit a given torque may have to be determined from the angle of twist rather than from the allowable unit stress. A shaft may be strong enough, but too flexible in order to perform properly.

The angle of twist of a shaft is given by

$$\theta = \frac{Tl}{E_sJ}$$

where θ = angle of twist, radians
$\quad T$ = torque, lb-in.
$\quad l$ = length, in.
$\quad E_s$ = modulus of elasticity in shear, psi
$\quad J$ = polar moment of inertia, in.^{4}

For a solid round shaft, the above formula reduces to

$$\theta = 10.2 \frac{Tl}{E_sd^4} \quad = \frac{2 S_s L}{E_s D}$$

To reduce θ to degrees, multiply by $180/\pi$ or 57.3, approximately.

The above expressions show that the angle of twist varies directly with the torque and length, and inversely with the modulus of elasticity in shear and with the polar moment of inertia (or the fourth power of the diameter, if J is replaced by d).

Example 10-1.   Calculate the minimum diameter a steel shaft 6 ft long may have in order to carry a torque of 80,000 lb-in. if the maximum shearing stress is not to exceed 8,000 psi and the angle of twist is not to exceed 1°.

SOLUTION:

1. Considering strength,

$$T = 0.196sd^3$$
$$80,000 = (0.196)(8,000)d^3$$
$$d^3 = 51$$
$$d = 3.708 \text{ in.}$$

2. Considering stiffness,

$$\theta = 10.2 \, \frac{Tl}{Esd^4}$$

$$\frac{\pi}{180} = \frac{(10.2)(80,000)(72)}{(12,000,000)d^4}$$

$$d^4 = 281$$
$$d = 4.09 \text{ in.}$$

Therefore stiffness rules and the shaft would be $4\frac{1}{8}$ in. diam.

PROBLEMS

10-10. Through what angle will the shaft of Prob. 10-3 be twisted in a length of 8 in.? E_s for steel = 12,000,000 psi.

10-11. A 2-in.-diam steel shaft 6 ft long is twisted by a force of 1,000 lb applied at a point 2 ft from its axis. Compute the unit shearing stress and angle of twist.

10-12. A steel shaft 6 in. diam is 8 ft long. Compute the torque and angle of twist if the maximum unit stress is not to exceed 8,000 psi.

10-13. Calculate the angle of twist for the shaft of Prob. 10-5 in a length of 2 ft.

10-14. Calculate the minimum diameter of a steel shaft 20 ft long which is to carry a torque of 80,000 lb-ft. The maximum shearing stress is not to exceed 7,500 psi, and the angle of twist is not to exceed 2° in 20 ft.

10-15. If the permissible angle of twist of a 3-in.-diam steel shaft is 2°, what length may it have if the maximum unit shear stress due to torsion is not to exceed 12,000 psi?

10-6. Torque, Horsepower, and RPM

Shafting is generally used to transmit power from a motor or engine to a machine. The work done by the motor is the product of the torque T and the angle θ through which the shaft turns. If the shaft is rotating at a constant speed against a resistance, the work done in one revolution is $2\pi T$. If N is the number of revolutions per minute at which the shaft is revolving, the work done in one minute is $2\pi TN$. Since horsepower is the amount of work done at the rate of 33,000 ft-lb per min or 396,000 in-lb per min, the number of horsepower is given by the expression

$$\text{hp} = \frac{2\pi TN}{396,000} = \frac{\pi TN}{198,000}$$

which is the horsepower formula for a solid circular shaft.

This expression may also be written in the form

$$T = \frac{198,000 \text{ hp}}{\pi N}$$

Since $T = 0.196sd^3$, the following useful relations between unit shear stress and horsepower for solid cylindrical shafts may be obtained:

$$\text{hp} = \frac{sd^3N}{321,000} \qquad s = \frac{321,000 \text{ hp}}{d^3N}$$

For a hollow shaft, the expression for horsepower is

$$\text{hp} = \frac{sN}{321,000}\left(\frac{d_1{}^4 - d_2{}^4}{d^1}\right)$$

where d_1 = outside diameter of shaft
d_2 = inside diameter of shaft

PROBLEMS

10-16. The torque in a 2-ft-diam solid steel shaft is 1,000,000 lb-ft. Compute the horsepower transmitted if it is rotating at 60 rpm.

10-17. Determine the horsepower a 3-in.-diam solid steel shaft will transmit at 150 rpm if the allowable torsional shear stress is 8,000 psi.

10-18. Determine the minimum diameter for a solid steel shaft which is to transmit 250 hp at 100 rpm. The allowable stress is 8,000 psi.

10-19. Determine the horsepower a steel tube with a 3 in. OD and 2¾ in. ID transmits at 3,400 rpm. Assume a maximum allowable torsional shear stress of 10,000 psi.

10-20. A solid steel shaft 1 in. diam is 8 in. long. Calculate the speed at which it must rotate to transmit 100 hp without exceeding a unit shear stress of 8,000 psi. Compute the angle of twist.

10-21. Calculate the speed at which a 2-in.-diam solid steel shaft 2 ft long must rotate to transmit 10 hp without exceeding a unit shear stress of 8,000 psi and an angle of twist of 1°.

10-22. A solid steel shaft 10 ft long is to transmit 120 hp at 50 rpm. The allowable unit shear stress is 10,000 psi and the angle of twist is not to exceed 2°. Calculate the proper diameter.

10-7. Flexure and Torsion Combined

Most line shafting carries a bending load as well as torque, thus combining tensile and compressive stresses with shear stresses. With such a combination, it can be shown that the maximum unit stress in tension and compression is given by the following expression:

$$s_{max} = \frac{S}{2} + \sqrt{\left(\frac{S}{2}\right)^2 + S_s^2}$$

where S = given unit stress in tension or compression

S_s = given unit stress in shear

Also, the maximum unit stress in shear is given as

$$s_{s\,max} = \sqrt{\left(\frac{S}{2}\right)^2 + S_s^2}$$

The flexure formula as previously stated is

$$\frac{M}{S} = \frac{I}{c} \qquad \text{or} \qquad S = M\frac{c}{I}$$

Since for a circular shaft, $I/c = J/2r$, then

$$S_s = \frac{Tc}{2I}$$

By substituting the above values for S and S_s

$$s_{max} = \frac{c}{2I} (M + \sqrt{M^2 + T^2})$$

or

$$s\frac{I}{c} = \frac{1}{2} (M + \sqrt{M^2 + T^2})$$

The expression $\frac{1}{2}(M + \sqrt{M^2 + T^2})$ is called the *equivalent bending moment*, M'. Then

$$\frac{M'}{s} = \frac{I}{c}$$

$$s = \frac{M'}{I/c}$$

$$M' = s\frac{I}{c}$$

Similarly,

$$s_s\frac{J}{r} = \sqrt{M^2 + T^2}$$

and the expression $\sqrt{M^2 + T^2}$ is called the *equivalent torque* T'. Then

$$\frac{T'}{s_s} = \frac{J}{r}$$

$$s_s = \frac{T'}{J/r}$$

$$T' = s_s\frac{J}{r}$$

10-8. Procedure for Designing Shafts

The following procedure may be followed in designing shafts:

1. Compute the torque T.
2. Compute the bending moment M.
3. Calculate the equivalent torque from $T' = \sqrt{M^2 + T^2}$.

4. Calculate the equivalent bending moment from

$$M' = \tfrac{1}{2}(M + \sqrt{M^2 + T^2})$$

5. Calculate the section modulus from $I/c = M'/s$.
6. Determine the diameter from $I/c = \pi d^3/32$.
7. Calculate the section modulus for shafts from

$$\frac{J}{r} = \frac{T'}{s_s}$$

8. Determine the diameter from $J/r = \pi d^3/8$.
9. The larger computed diameter determines the proper size shaft.

Example 10-2.   Calculate the size shaft required to transmit 250 hp at 100 rpm while subjected to a bending moment of 50,000 lb-in. The allowable unit stresses are 18,000 psi in tension and compression and 10,000 psi in shear.

SOLUTION:

1. Torque:

$$T = \frac{198,000}{\pi N}\,\mathrm{hp} = \frac{(198,000)(250)}{(3.14)(100)} = 158,000\ \mathrm{lb\text{-}in.}$$

2. Bending moment: $M = 50,000$ lb-in.
3. $T' = \sqrt{M^2 + T^2} = \sqrt{(50,000)^2 + (158,000)^2}$
$$= 166,000\ \mathrm{lb\text{-}in.}$$
4. $M' = \tfrac{1}{2}(M + \sqrt{M^2 + T^2}) = \tfrac{1}{2}(50,000 + 166,000)$
$$= 108,000\ \mathrm{lb\text{-}in.}$$

5.
$$\frac{I}{c} = \frac{M'}{s}$$
$$\frac{I}{c} = \frac{108,000}{18,000} = 6\ \mathrm{in.}^3$$

6.
$$\frac{I}{c} = \frac{\pi d^3}{32}$$
$$6 = \frac{(3.14)d^3}{32}$$
$$d = 3.9\ \mathrm{in.}$$

7.
$$\frac{J}{r} = \frac{T'}{s_s}$$

$$\frac{J}{r} = \frac{166,000}{10,000} = 16.6 \text{ in.}^3$$

8.
$$\frac{J}{r} = \frac{\pi d^3}{8}$$

$$16.6 = \frac{(3.14)d^3}{8}$$

$$d = 3.48 \text{ in.}$$

9. The larger computed diameter is 3.9 in., so that a shaft 4.0 in. diam will be required.

PROBLEMS

10-23. Design a shaft to transmit 200 hp at 60 rpm while subjected to a bending moment of 5,000 lb-ft. The allowable unit stresses are 18,000 psi in tension, 16,000 psi in compression, 8,000 psi in shear.

10-24. If the shaft in Prob. 10-23 is 5 ft long and there is an additional specification that the angle of twist must not exceed 2°, will the shaft be safe?

10-25. A solid steel shaft 8 ft long is to transmit 300 hp at 50 rpm while subjected to a bending moment of 4,000 lb-ft. Calculate the size of shaft required if the angle of twist is not to exceed 1°. The allowable unit stresses are 15,000 psi in tension and compression and 8,000 psi in shear.

10-26. A steel shaft 6 ft long has a 24-in. pulley located at its midpoint which produces a force of 1,000 lb as it rotates at a constant speed of 100 rpm. The angle of twist must not exceed 2°. The allowable unit stresses are 15,000 psi in tension and compression and 10,000 psi in shear. Calculate the size of shaft required.

10-27. A 6-in.-diam shaft transmits a torque of 100,000 lb-in. and is subjected to a bending moment of 8,000 lb-ft. Calculate the unit stresses developed in shear, compression, and tension.

10-9. Helical Springs

The elongation and compression of a helical spring offers another excellent example of torsion. A helical spring is made by wrapping wire around a cylinder.   When the spring is to be used in tension, its ends are turned into hooks in toward the center in order to apply the force axially.   If the spring is to be used in compression, these hooks are omitted and the end coils are made normal to the axis of the spring in order to distribute the load properly.

Figure 10-4 shows a helical spring with a load P which causes the spring to elongate.   The entire wire is subjected to

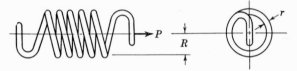

Fig. 10-4.   Helical spring.

a torque $T = PR$.   The total elongation is equal to the product of the angle of twist and the radius of the coil.   In algebraic form, $l = R\theta$.

If there are n coils in the length l, then $l = 2\pi R n$.   Since $\theta = Tl/E_s J$, by substituting values of T, l, and J, the elongation of a helical spring is given by the formula

$$l = \frac{64PR^3 n}{E_s d^4}$$

Example 10-3.   A $\frac{1}{4}$-in.-diam wire is used to make a helical spring of 10 coils.   The radius of the coil from the axis to the center of all sections is 2 in.   Calculate the elongation due to a load of 5 lb if the modulus of rigidity is 12,000,000 psi.

Solution:

$$l = \frac{64PR^3 n}{E_s d^4}$$

$$l = \frac{64.5(2)^3 10}{(12,000,000)(0.0039)}$$

$$l = 0.55 \text{ in.}$$

PROBLEMS

10-28. A $\frac{1}{2}$-in.-diam steel wire is used to make a helical spring of 20 coils by wrapping the wire around a cylinder $5\frac{1}{2}$ in. diam. Calculate the elongation due to a load of 25 lb. The modulus of rigidity $E_s = 12,000,000$ psi.

10-29. If s_s is the allowable unit shear stress, derive the expression for the elongation of a spring in terms of s_s, E_s, R, d, and n.

10-30. Find the unit shearing stress in Example 10-3.

10-31. Find the unit shearing stress in Prob. 10-28.

10-32. Determine the elongation of a spring given the following data:

> Allowable unit shearing stress = 4,000 psi
> Diameter of spring = $\frac{1}{2}$ in.
> Number of coils = 12
> Radius of coils = 5 in.
> Modulus of rigidity = 15,000,000 psi

APPENDIX

Table 1

WF SHAPES

PROPERTIES FOR DESIGNING

Nominal Size	Weight per Foot	Area	Depth	Flange Width	Flange Thickness	Web Thickness	AXIS X-X I	AXIS X-X S	AXIS X-X r	AXIS Y-Y I	AXIS Y-Y S	AXIS Y-Y r
In.	Lb.	In.^{2}	In.	In.	In.	In.	In.^{4}	In.^{3}	In.	In.^{4}	In.^{3}	In.
27 x 14	177	52.10	27.31	14.090	1.190	.725	6728.6	492.8	11.36	518.9	73.7	3.16
	160	47.04	27.08	14.023	1.075	.658	6018.6	444.5	11.31	458.0	65.3	3.12
	145	42.68	26.88	13.965	.975	.600	5414.3	402.9	11.26	406.9	58.3	3.09
27 x 10	114	33.53	27.28	10.070	.932	.570	4080.5	299.2	11.03	149.6	29.7	2.11
	102	30.01	27.07	10.018	.827	.518	3604.1	266.3	10.96	129.5	25.9	2.08
	94	27.65	26.91	9.990	.747	.490	3266.7	242.8	10.87	115.1	23.0	2.04
24 x 14	160	47.04	24.72	14.091	1.135	.656	5110.3	413.5	10.42	492.6	69.9	3.23
	145	42.62	24.49	14.043	1.020	.608	4561.0	372.5	10.34	434.3	61.8	3.19
	130	38.21	24.25	14.000	.900	.565	4009.5	330.7	10.24	375.2	53.6	3.13
24 x 12	120	35.29	24.31	12.088	.930	.556	3635.3	299.1	10.15	254.0	42.0	2.68
	110	32.36	24.16	12.042	.855	.510	3315.0	274.4	10.12	229.1	38.0	2.66
	100	29.43	24.00	12.000	.775	.468	2987.3	248.9	10.08	203.5	33.9	2.63
24 x 9	94	27.63	24.29	9.061	.872	.516	2683.0	220.9	9.85	102.2	22.6	1.92
	84	24.71	24.09	9.015	.772	.470	2364.3	196.3	9.78	88.3	19.6	1.89
	76	22.37	23.91	8.985	.682	.440	2096.4	175.4	9.68	76.5	17.0	1.85
21 x 13	142	41.76	21.46	13.132	1.095	.659	3403.1	317.2	9.03	385.9	58.8	3.04
	127	37.34	21.24	13.061	.985	.588	3017.2	284.1	8.99	338.6	51.8	3.01
	112	32.93	21.00	13.000	.865	.527	2620.6	249.6	8.92	289.7	44.6	2.96
21 x 9	96	28.21	21.14	9.038	.935	.575	2088.9	197.6	8.60	109.3	24.2	1.97
	82	24.10	20.86	8.962	.795	.499	1752.4	168.0	8.53	89.6	20.0	1.93
21 x 8¼	73	21.46	21.24	8.295	.740	.455	1600.3	150.7	8.64	66.2	16.0	1.76
	68	20.02	21.13	8.270	.685	.430	1478.3	139.9	8.59	60.4	14.6	1.74
	62	18.23	20.99	8.240	.615	.400	1326.8	126.4	8.53	53.1	12.9	1.71

Table 1 (*continued*)

W⁻ SHAPES

PROPERTIES FOR DESIGNING

Nominal Size	Weight per Foot	Area	Depth	Flange Width	Flange Thickness	Web Thickness	AXIS X-X I	AXIS X-X S	AXIS X-X r	AXIS Y-Y I	AXIS Y-Y S	AXIS Y-Y r
In.	Lb.	In.²	In.	In.	In.	In.	In.⁴	In.³	In.	In.⁴	In.³	In.
18 x 11¾	114	33.51	18.48	11.833	.991	.595	2033.8	220.1	7.79	255.6	43.2	2.76
	105	30.86	18.32	11.792	.911	.554	1852.5	202.2	7.75	231.0	39.2	2.73
	96	28.22	18.16	11.750	.831	.512	1674.7	184.4	7.70	206.8	35.2	2.71
18 x 8¾	85	24.97	18.32	8.838	.911	.526	1429.9	156.1	7.57	99.4	22.5	2.00
	77	22.63	18.16	8.787	.831	.475	1286.8	141.7	7.54	88.6	20.2	1.98
	70	20.56	18.00	8.750	.751	.438	1153.9	128.2	7.49	78.5	17.9	1.95
	64	18.80	17.87	8.715	.686	.403	1045.8	117.0	7.46	70.3	16.1	1.93
18 x 7½	60	17.64	18.25	7.558	.695	.416	984.0	107.8	7.47	47.1	12.5	1.63
	55	16.19	18.12	7.532	.630	.390	889.9	98.2	7.41	42.0	11.1	1.61
	50	14.71	18.00	7.500	.570	.358	800.6	89.0	7.38	37.2	9.9	1.59
16 x 11½	96	28.22	16.32	11.533	.875	.535	1355.1	166.1	6.93	207.2	35.9	2.71
	88	25.87	16.16	11.502	.795	.504	1222.6	151.3	6.87	185.2	32.2	2.67
16 x 8½	78	22.92	16.32	8.586	.875	.529	1042.6	127.8	6.74	87.5	20.4	1.95
	71	20.86	16.16	8.543	.795	.486	936.9	115.9	6.70	77.9	18.2	1.93
	64	18.80	16.00	8.500	.715	.443	833.8	104.2	6.66	68.4	16.1	1.91
	58	17.04	15.86	8.464	.645	.407	746.4	94.1	6.62	60.5	14.3	1.88
16 x 7	50	14.70	16.25	7.073	.628	.380	655.4	80.7	6.68	34.8	9.8	1.54
	45	13.24	16.12	7.039	.563	.346	583.3	72.4	6.64	30.5	8.7	1.52
	40	11.77	16.00	7.000	.503	.307	515.5	64.4	6.62	26.5	7.6	1.50
	36	10.59	15.85	6.992	.428	.299	446.3	56.3	6.49	22.1	6.3	1.45
14 x 14½	95	27.94	14.12	14.545	.748	.465	1063.5	150.6	6.17	383.7	52.8	3.71
	87	25.56	14.00	14.500	.688	.420	966.9	138.1	6.15	349.7	48.2	3.70
14 x 12	84	24.71	14.18	12.023	.778	.451	928.4	130.9	6.13	225.5	37.5	3.02
	78	22.94	14.06	12.000	.718	.428	851.2	121.1	6.09	206.9	34.5	3.00
14 x 10	74	21.76	14.19	10.072	.783	.450	796.8	112.3	6.05	133.5	26.5	2.48
	68	20.00	14.06	10.040	.718	.418	724.1	103.0	6.02	121.2	24.1	2.46
	61	17.94	13.91	10.000	.643	.378	641.5	92.2	5.98	107.3	21.5	2.45

Table 1 (*continued*)

WF SHAPES

PROPERTIES FOR DESIGNING

Nominal Size	Weight per Foot	Area	Depth	Flange		Web Thick-ness	AXIS X-X			AXIS Y-Y		
				Width	Thick-ness		I	S	r	I	S	r
In.	Lb.	In.²	In.	In.	In.	In.	In.⁴	In.³	In.	In.⁴	In.³	In.
14 x 8	53	15.59	13.94	8.062	.658	.370	542.1	77.8	5.90	57.5	14.3	1.92
	48	14.11	13.81	8.031	.593	.339	484.9	70.2	5.86	51.3	12.8	1.91
	43	12.65	13.68	8.000	.528	.308	429.0	62.7	5.82	45.1	11.3	1.89
14 x 6¾	38	11.17	14.12	6.776	.513	.313	385.3	54.6	5.87	24.6	7.3	1.49
	34	10.00	13.98	6.750	.453	.287	339.2	48.5	5.83	21.3	6.3	1.46
	30	8.81	13.86	6.733	.383	.270	289.6	41.8	5.73	17.5	5.2	1.41
12 x 12	190	55.86	14.38	12.670	1.736	1.060	1892.5	263.2	5.82	589.7	93.1	3.25
	161	47.38	13.88	12.515	1.486	.905	1541.8	222.2	5.70	486.2	77.7	3.20
	133	39.11	13.38	12.365	1.236	.755	1221.2	182.5	5.59	389.9	63.1	3.16
	120	35.31	13.12	12.320	1.106	.710	1071.7	163.4	5.51	345.1	56.0	3.13
	106	31.19	12.88	12.230	.986	.620	930.7	144.5	5.46	300.9	49.2	3.11
	99	29.09	12.75	12.190	.921	.580	858.5	134.7	5.43	278.2	45.7	3.09
	92	27.06	12.62	12.155	.856	.545	788.9	125.0	5.40	256.4	42.2	3.08
	85	24.98	12.50	12.105	.796	.495	723.3	115.7	5.38	235.5	38.9	3.07
	79	23.22	12.38	12.080	.736	.470	663.0	107.1	5.34	216.4	35.8	3.05
	72	21.16	12.25	12.040	.671	.430	597.4	97.5	5.31	195.3	32.4	3.04
	65	19.11	12.12	12.000	.606	.390	533.4	88.0	5.28	174.6	29.1	3.02
12 x 10	58	17.06	12.19	10.014	.641	.359	476.1	78.1	5.28	107.4	21.4	2.51
	53	15.59	12.06	10.000	.576	.345	426.2	70.7	5.23	96.1	19.2	2.48
12 x 8	50	14.71	12.19	8.077	.641	.371	394.5	64.7	5.18	56.4	14.0	1.96
	45	13.24	12.06	8.042	.576	.336	350.8	58.2	5.15	50.0	12.4	1.94
	40	11.77	11.94	8.000	.516	.294	310.1	51.9	5.13	44.1	11.0	1.94
12 x 6½	36	10.59	12.24	6.565	.540	.305	280.8	45.9	5.15	23.7	7.2	1.50
	31	9.12	12.09	6.525	.465	.265	238.4	39.4	5.11	19.8	6.1	1.47
	27	7.97	11.95	6.500	.400	.240	204.1	34.1	5.06	16.6	5.1	1.44

The Appendix tables are reprinted with permission from "Steel Construction," the manual of the American Institute of Steel Construction.

Table 1 (continued)

W SHAPES

PROPERTIES FOR DESIGNING

Nominal Size	Weight per Foot	Area	Depth	Flange Width	Flange Thickness	Web Thickness	AXIS X-X I	AXIS X-X S	AXIS X-X r	AXIS Y-Y I	AXIS Y-Y S	AXIS Y-Y r
In.	Lb.	In.^{2}	In.	In.	In.	In.	In.^{4}	In.^{3}	In.	In.^{4}	In.^{3}	In.
10 x 10	112	32.92	11.38	10.415	1.248	.755	718.7	126.3	4.67	235.4	45.2	2.67
	100	29.43	11.12	10.345	1.118	.685	625.0	112.4	4.61	206.6	39.9	2.65
	89	26.19	10.88	10.275	.998	.615	542.4	99.7	4.55	180.6	35.2	2.63
	77	22.67	10.62	10.195	.868	.535	457.2	86.1	4.49	153.4	30.1	2.60
	72	21.18	10.50	10.170	.808	.510	420.7	80.1	4.46	141.8	27.9	2.59
	66	19.41	10.38	10.117	.748	.457	382.5	73.7	4.44	129.2	25.5	2.58
	60	17.66	10.25	10.075	.683	.415	343.7	67.1	4.41	116.5	23.1	2.57
	54	15.88	10.12	10.028	.618	.368	305.7	60.4	4.39	103.9	20.7	2.56
	49	14.40	10.00	10.000	.558	.340	272.9	54.6	4.35	93.0	18.6	2.54
10 x 8	45	13.24	10.12	8.022	.618	.350	248.6	49.1	4.33	53.2	13.3	2.00
	39	11.48	9.94	7.990	.528	.318	209.7	42.2	4.27	44.9	11.2	1.98
	33	9.71	9.75	7.964	.433	.292	170.9	35.0	4.20	36.5	9.2	1.94
10 x 5¾	29	8.53	10.22	5.799	.500	.289	157.3	30.8	4.29	15.2	5.2	1.34
	25	7.35	10.08	5.762	.430	.252	133.2	26.4	4.26	12.7	4.4	1.31
	21	6.19	9.90	5.750	.340	.240	106.3	21.5	4.14	9.7	3.4	1.25
8 x 8	67	19.70	9.00	8.287	.933	.575	271.8	60.4	3.71	88.6	21.4	2.12
	58	17.06	8.75	8.222	.808	.510	227.3	52.0	3.65	74.9	18.2	2.10
	48	14.11	8.50	8.117	.683	.405	183.7	43.2	3.61	60.9	15.0	2.08
	40	11.76	8.25	8.077	.558	.365	146.3	35.5	3.53	49.0	12.1	2.04
	35	10.30	8.12	8.027	.493	.315	126.5	31.1	3.50	42.5	10.6	2.03
	31	9.12	8.00	8.000	.433	.288	109.7	27.4	3.47	37.0	9.2	2.01
8 x 6½	28	8.23	8.06	6.540	.463	.285	97.8	24.3	3.45	21.6	6.6	1.62
	24	7.06	7.93	6.500	.398	.245	82.5	20.8	3.42	18.2	5.6	1.61
8 x 5¼	20	5.88	8.14	5.268	.378	.248	69.2	17.0	3.43	8.5	3.2	1.20
	17	5.00	8.00	5.250	.308	.230	56.4	14.1	3.36	6.7	2.6	1.16

Table 2

WF SHAPES
MISCELLANEOUS (B)
COLUMNS AND BEAMS

PROPERTIES FOR DESIGNING

Nominal Size	Weight per Foot	Area	Depth	Flange Width	Flange Thickness	Web Thickness	AXIS X-X I	AXIS X-X S	AXIS X-X r	AXIS Y-Y I	AXIS Y-Y S	AXIS Y-Y r
In.	Lb.	In.²	In.	In.	In.	In.	In.⁴	In.³	In.	In.⁴	In.³	In.
WF SHAPES AND LIGHT COLUMNS												
6 WF	25	7 37	6.37	6.080	.456	.320	53.5	16.8	2.69	17.1	5.6	1.52
6 x 6	20	5.90	6.20	6.018	.367	.258	41.7	13.4	2.66	13.3	4.4	1.50
	15.5	4.62	6.00	6.000	.269	.240	30.3	10.1	2.56	9.69	3.2	1.45
5 WF	18.5	5.45	5.12	5.025	.420	.265	25.4	9.94	2.16	8.89	3.54	1.28
5 x 5	16	4.70	5.00	5.000	.360	.240	21.3	8.53	2.13	7.51	3.00	1.26
4 WF	13	3.82	4.16	4.060	.345	.280	11.3	5.45	1.72	3.76	1.85	.99
LIGHT BEAMS												
12 x 4	22	6.47	12.31	4.030	.424	.260	155.7	25.3	4.91	4.55	2.26	.84
	19	5.62	12.16	4.010	.349	.240	130.1	21.4	4.81	3.67	1.83	.81
	16½	4.86	12.00	4.000	.269	.230	105.3	17.5	4.65	2.79	1.39	.76
10 x 4	19	5.61	10.25	4.020	.394	.250	96.2	18.8	4.14	4.19	2.08	.86
	17	4.98	10.12	4.010	.329	.240	81.8	16.2	4.05	3.45	1.72	.83
	15	4.40	10.00	4.000	.269	.230	68.8	13.8	3.95	2.79	1.39	.80
8 x 4	15	4.43	8.12	4.015	.314	.245	48.0	11.8	3.29	3.30	1.65	.86
	13	3.83	8.00	4.000	.254	.230	39.5	9.88	3.21	2.62	1.31	.83
6 x 4	16	4.72	6.25	4.030	.404	.260	31.7	10.1	2.59	4.32	2.14	.96
	12	3.53	6.00	4.000	.279	.230	21.7	7.24	2.48	2.89	1.44	.90
JOISTS												
12 x 4	14	4.14	11.91	3.970	.224	.200	88.2	14.8	4.61	2.25	1.13	.74
10 x 4	11½	3.39	9.87	3.950	.204	.180	51.9	10.5	3.92	2.01	1.02	.77
8 x 4	10	2.95	7.90	3.940	.204	.170	30.8	7.79	3.23	1.99	1.01	.82
6 x 4	8½	2.50	5.83	3.940	.194	.170	14.8	5.07	2.43	1.89	.96	.87

Above shapes all rolled by Bethlehem Steel Co. and Carnegie-Illinois Steel Corp., except 4 WF 13 by Bethlehem Steel Co. only.

Table 3

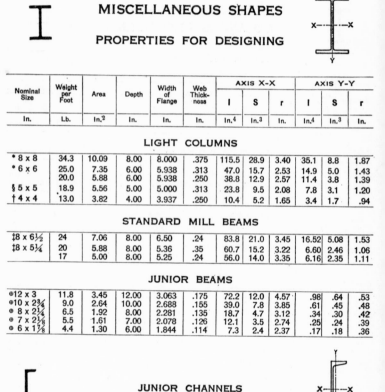

MISCELLANEOUS SHAPES
PROPERTIES FOR DESIGNING

Nominal Size	Weight per Foot	Area	Depth	Width of Flange	Web Thick-ness	AXIS X-X			AXIS Y-Y		
						I	S	r	I	S	r
In.	Lb.	In.²	In.	In.	In.	In.⁴	In.³	In.	In.⁴	In.³	In.
LIGHT COLUMNS											
* 8 x 8	34.3	10.09	8.00	8.000	.375	115.5	28.9	3.40	35.1	8.8	1.87
* 6 x 6	25.0	7.35	6.00	5.938	.313	47.0	15.7	2.53	14.9	5.0	1.43
	20.0	5.88	6.00	5.938	.250	38.8	12.9	2.57	11.4	3.8	1.39
§ 5 x 5	18.9	5.56	5.00	5.000	.313	23.8	9.5	2.08	7.8	3.1	1.20
† 4 x 4	13.0	3.82	4.00	3.937	.250	10.4	5.2	1.65	3.4	1.7	.94
STANDARD MILL BEAMS											
‡8 x 6½	24	7.06	8.00	6.50	.24	83.8	21.0	3.45	16.52	5.08	1.53
‡8 x 5¼	20	5.88	8.00	5.36	.35	60.7	15.2	3.22	6.60	2.46	1.06
	17	5.00	8.00	5.25	.24	56.0	14.0	3.35	6.16	2.35	1.11
JUNIOR BEAMS											
⊕12 x 3	11.8	3.45	12.00	3.063	.175	72.2	12.0	4.57	.98	.64	.53
⊕10 x 2¾	9.0	2.64	10.00	2.688	.155	39.0	7.8	3.85	.61	.45	.48
⊕ 8 x 2¼	6.5	1.92	8.00	2.281	.135	18.7	4.7	3.12	.34	.30	.42
⊕ 7 x 2⅛	5.5	1.61	7.00	2.078	.126	12.1	3.5	2.74	.25	.24	.39
⊕ 6 x 1⅞	4.4	1.30	6.00	1.844	.114	7.3	2.4	2.37	.17	.18	.36

JUNIOR CHANNELS

Nominal Size	Weight per Foot	Area	Depth	Width of Flange	Web Thick-ness	AXIS X-X			AXIS Y-Y			
						I	S	r	I	S	r	.x
In.	Lb.	In.²	In.	In.	In.	In.⁴	In.³	In.	In.⁴	In.³	In.	In.
⊕12 x 1½	10.6	3.12	12.00	1.500	.190	55.8	9.3	4.23	.39	.32	.35	.27
⊕10 x 1½	8.4	2.47	10.00	1.500	.170	32.3	6.5	3.61	.33	.28	.37	.29
⊕10 x 1⅛	6.5	1.91	10.00	1.125	.150	22.1	4.4	3.47	.12	.13	.25	.19

*Rolled by Carnegie-Illinois Steel Corp. and Inland Steel Co.
§Rolled by Carnegie-Illinois Steel Corp. and Bethlehem Steel Co.-M.
†Rolled by Carnegie-Illinois Steel Corp.-M.
‡Rolled by The Phoenix Iron Co.-B.
⊕Rolled by Jones & Laughlin Steel Corp.-Jr.

Table 4

AMERICAN STANDARD BEAMS

PROPERTIES FOR DESIGNING

Nominal Size	Weight per Foot	Area	Depth	Flange		Web Thickness	AXIS X-X			AXIS Y-Y		
				Width	Thickness		I	S	r	I	S	r
In.	Lb.	In.^{2}	In.	In.	In.	In.	In.^{4}	In.^{3}	In.	In.^{4}	In.^{3}	In.
24 x 7⅞	120.0	35.13	24.00	8.048	1.102	.798	3010.8	250.9	9.26	84.9	21.1	1.56
	105.9	30.98	24.00	7.875	1.102	.625	2811.5	234.3	9.53	78.9	20.0	1.60
24 x 7	100.0	29.25	24.00	7.247	.871	.747	2371.8	197.6	9.05	48.4	13.4	1.29
	90.0	26.30	24.00	7.124	.871	.624	2230.1	185.8	9.21	45.5	12.8	1.32
	79.9	23.33	24.00	7.000	.871	.500	2087.2	173.9	9.46	42.9	12.2	1.36
20 x 7	95.0	27.74	20.00	7.200	.916	.800	1599.7	160.0	7.59	50.5	14.0	1.35
	85.0	24.80	20.00	7.053	.916	.653	1501.7	150.2	7.78	47.0	13.3	1.38
20 x 6¼	75.0	21.90	20.00	6.391	.789	.641	1263.5	126.3	7.60	30.1	9.4	1.17
	65.4	19.08	20.00	6.250	.789	.500	1169.5	116.9	7.83	27.9	8.9	1.21
18 x 6	70.0	20.46	18.00	6.251	.691	.711	917.5	101.9	6.70	24.5	7.8	1.09
	54.7	15.94	18.00	6.000	.691	.460	795.5	88.4	7.07	21.2	7.1	1.15
15 x 5½	50.0	14.59	15.00	5.640	.622	.550	481.1	64.2	5.74	16.0	5.7	1.05
	42.9	12.49	15.00	5.500	.622	.410	441.8	58.9	5.95	14.6	5.3	1.08
12 x 5¼	50.0	14.57	12.00	5.477	.659	.687	301.6	50.3	4.55	16.0	5.8	1.05
	40.8	11.84	12.00	5.250	.659	.460	268.9	44.8	4.77	13.8	5.3	1.08
12 x 5	35.0	10.20	12.00	5.078	.544	.428	227.0	37.8	4.72	10.0	3.9	.99
	31.8	9.26	12.00	5.000	.544	.350	215.8	36.0	4.83	9.5	3.8	1.01
10 x 4⅝	35.0	10.22	10.00	4.944	.491	.594	145.8	29.2	3.78	8.5	3.4	.91
	25.4	7.38	10.00	4.660	.491	.310	122.1	24.4	4.07	6.9	3.0	.97
8 x 4	23.0	6.71	8.00	4.171	.425	.441	64.2	16.0	3.09	4.4	2.1	.81
	18.4	5.34	8.00	4.000	.425	.270	56.9	14.2	3.26	3.8	1.9	.84
7 x 3⅝	20.0	5.83	7.00	3.860	.392	.450	41.9	12.0	2.68	3.1	1.6	.74
	15.3	4.43	7.00	3.660	.392	.250	36.2	10.4	2.86	2.7	1.5	.78
6 x 3⅜	17.25	5.02	6.00	3.565	.359	.465	26.0	8.7	2.28	2.3	1.3	.68
	12.5	3.61	6.00	3.330	.359	.230	21.8	7.3	2.46	1.8	1.1	.72
5 x 3	14.75	4.29	5.00	3.284	.326	.494	15.0	6.0	1.87	1.7	1.0	.63
	10.0	2.87	5.00	3.000	.326	.210	12.1	4.8	2.05	1.2	.82	.65
4 x 2⅝	9.5	2.76	4.00	2.796	.293	.326	6.7	3.3	1.56	.91	.65	.58
	7.7	2.21	4.00	2.660	.293	.190	6.0	3.0	1.64	.77	.58	.59
3 x 2⅜	7.5	2.17	3.00	2.509	.260	.349	2.9	1.9	1.15	.59	.47	.52
	5.7	1.64	3.00	2.330	.260	.170	2.5	1.7	1.23	.46	.40	.53

Table 5

AMERICAN STANDARD CHANNELS

PROPERTIES FOR DESIGNING

Nominal Size	Weight per Foot	Area	Depth	Flange		Web Thickness	AXIS X-X			AXIS Y-Y			x
				Width	Average Thickness		I	S	r	I	S	r	
In.	Lb.	In.²	In.	In.	In.	In.	In.⁴	In.³	In.	In.⁴	In.³	In.	In.
*18 x 4	58.0	16.98	18.00	4.200	.625	.700	670.7	74.5	6.29	18.5	5.6	1.04	.88
	51.9	15.18	18.00	4.100	.625	.600	622.1	69.1	6.40	17.1	5.3	1.06	.87
	45.8	13.38	18.00	4.000	.625	.500	573.5	63.7	6.55	15.8	5.1	1.09	.89
	42.7	12.48	18.00	3.950	.625	.450	549.2	61.0	6.64	15.0	4.9	1.10	.90
15 x 3⅜	50.0	14.64	15.00	3.716	.650	.716	401.4	53.6	5.24	11.2	3.8	.87	.80
	40.0	11.70	15.00	3.520	.650	.520	346.3	46.2	5.44	9.3	3.4	.89	.78
	33.9	9.90	15.00	3.400	.650	.400	312.6	41.7	5.62	8.2	3.2	.91	.79
12 x 3	30.0	8.79	12.00	3.170	.501	.510	161.2	26.9	4.28	5.2	2.1	.77	.68
	25.0	7.32	12.00	3.047	.501	.387	143.5	23.9	4.43	4.5	1.9	.79	.68
	20.7	6.03	12.00	2.940	.501	.280	128.1	21.4	4.61	3.9	1.7	.81	.70
10 x 2⅝	30.0	8.80	10.00	3.033	.436	.673	103.0	20.6	3.42	4.0	1.7	.67	.65
	25.0	7.33	10.00	2.886	.436	.526	90.7	18.1	3.52	3.4	1.5	.68	.62
	20.0	5.86	10.00	2.739	.436	.379	78.5	15.7	3.66	2.8	1.3	.70	.61
	15.3	4.47	10.00	2.600	.436	.240	66.9	13.4	3.87	2.3	1.2	.72	.64
9 x 2½	20.0	5.86	9.00	2.648	.413	.448	60.6	13.5	3.22	2.4	1.2	.65	.59
	15.0	4.39	9.00	2.485	.413	.285	50.7	11.3	3.40	1.9	1.0	.67	.59
	13.4	3.89	9.00	2.430	.413	.230	47.3	10.5	3.49	1.8	.97	.67	.61
8 x 2¼	18.75	5.49	8.00	2.527	.390	.487	43.7	10.9	2.82	2.0	1.0	.60	.57
	13.75	4.02	8.00	2.343	.390	.303	35.8	9.0	2.99	1.5	.86	.62	.56
	11.5	3.36	8.00	2.260	.390	.220	32.3	8.1	3.10	1.3	.79	.63	.58
7 x 2⅛	14.75	4.32	7.00	2.299	.366	.419	27.1	7.7	2.51	1.4	.79	.57	.53
	12.25	3.58	7.00	2.194	.366	.314	24.1	6.9	2.59	1.2	.71	.58	.53
	9.8	2.85	7.00	2.090	.366	.210	21.1	6.0	2.72	.98	.63	.59	.55
6 x 2	13.0	3.81	6.00	2.157	.343	.437	17.3	5.8	2.13	1.1	.65	.53	.52
	10.5	3.07	6.00	2.034	.343	.314	15.1	5.0	2.22	.87	.57	.53	.50
	8.2	2.39	6.00	1.920	.343	.200	13.0	4.3	2.34	.70	.50	.54	.52
5 x 1¾	9.0	2.63	5.00	1.885	.320	.325	8.8	3.5	1.83	.64	.45	.49	.48
	6.7	1.95	5.00	1.750	.320	.190	7.4	3.0	1.95	.48	.38	.50	.49
4 x 1⅝	7.25	2.12	4.00	1.720	.296	.320	4.5	2.3	1.47	.44	.35	.46	.46
	5.4	1.56	4.00	1.580	.296	.180	3.8	1.9	1.56	.32	.29	.45	.46
3 x 1½	6.0	1.75	3.00	1.596	.273	.356	2.1	1.4	1.08	.31	.27	.42	.46
	5.0	1.46	3.00	1.498	.273	.258	1.8	1.2	1.12	.25	.24	.41	.44
	4.1	1.19	3.00	1.410	.273	.170	1.6	1.1	1.17	.20	.21	.41	.44

*Car and Shipbuilding Channel; not an American Standard.

Table 6

ANGLES
EQUAL LEGS

PROPERTIES FOR DESIGNING

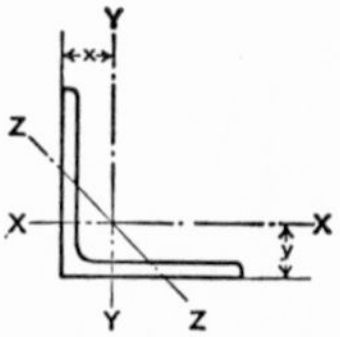

Size	Thickness	Weight per Foot	Area	AXIS X-X AND AXIS Y-Y				AXIS Z-Z
				I	S	r	x or y	r
In.	In.	Lb.	In.²	In.⁴	In.³	In.	In.	In.
8 x 8	1⅛	56.9	16.73	98.0	17.5	2.42	2.41	1.56
	1	51.0	15.00	89.0	15.8	2.44	2.37	1.56
	⅞	45.0	13.23	79.6	14.0	2.45	2.32	1.57
	¾	38.9	11.44	69.7	12.2	2.47	2.28	1.57
	⅝	32.7	9.61	59.4	10.3	2.49	2.23	1.58
	⁹⁄₁₆	29.6	8.68	54.1	9.3	2.50	2.21	1.58
	½	26.4	7.75	48.6	8.4	2.50	2.19	1.59
6 x 6	1	37.4	11.00	35.5	8.6	1.80	1.86	1.17
	⅞	33.1	9.73	31.9	7.6	1.81	1.82	1.17
	¾	28.7	8.44	28.2	6.7	1.83	1.78	1.17
	⅝	24.2	7.11	24.2	5.7	1.84	1.73	1.18
	⁹⁄₁₆	21.9	6.43	22.1	5.1	1.85	1.71	1.18
	½	19.6	5.75	19.9	4.6	1.86	1.68	1.18
	⁷⁄₁₆	17.2	5.06	17.7	4.1	1.87	1.66	1.19
	⅜	14.9	4.36	15.4	3.5	1.88	1.64	1.19
	⁵⁄₁₆	12.5	3.66	13.0	3.0	1.89	1.61	1.19
5 x 5	⅞	27.2	7.98	17.8	5.2	1.49	1.57	.97
	¾	23.6	6.94	15.7	4.5	1.51	1.52	.97
	⅝	20.0	5.86	13.6	3.9	1.52	1.48	.98
	½	16.2	4.75	11.3	3.2	1.54	1.43	.98
	⁷⁄₁₆	14.3	4.18	10.0	2.8	1.55	1.41	.98
	⅜	12.3	3.61	8.7	2.4	1.56	1.39	.99
	⁵⁄₁₆	10.3	3.03	7.4	2.0	1.57	1.37	.99
4 x 4	¾	18.5	5.44	7.7	2.8	1.19	1.27	.78
	⅝	15.7	4.61	6.7	2.4	1.20	1.23	.78
	½	12.8	3.75	5.6	2.0	1.22	1.18	.78
	⁷⁄₁₆	11.3	3.31	5.0	1.8	1.23	1.16	.78
	⅜	9.8	2.86	4.4	1.5	1.23	1.14	.79
	⁵⁄₁₆	8.2	2.40	3.7	1.3	1.24	1.12	.79
	¼	6.6	1.94	3.0	1.1	1.25	1.09	.80

Table 6 (*continued*)

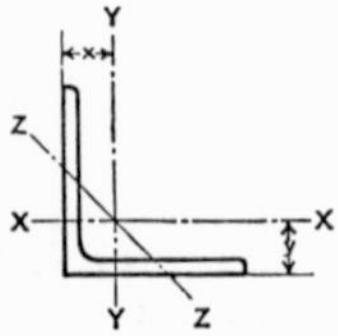

ANGLES
EQUAL LEGS

PROPERTIES FOR DESIGNING

Size	Thickness	Weight per Foot	Area	AXIS X-X AND AXIS Y-Y				AXIS Z-Z
				I	S	r	x or y	r
In.	In.	Lb.	In.²	In.⁴	In.³	In.	In.	In.
3½ x 3½	½	11.1	3.25	3.6	1.5	1.06	1.06	.68
	7/16	9.8	2.87	3.3	1.3	1.07	1.04	.68
	3/8	8.5	2.48	2.9	1.2	1.07	1.01	.69
	5/16	7.2	2.09	2.5	.98	1.08	.99	.69
	¼	5.8	1.69	2.0	.79	1.09	.97	.69
3 x 3	½	9.4	2.75	2.2	1.1	.90	.93	.58
	7/16	8.3	2.43	2.0	.95	.91	.91	.58
	3/8	7.2	2.11	1.8	.83	.91	.89	.58
	5/16	6.1	1.78	1.5	.71	.92	.87	.59
	¼	4.9	1.44	1.2	.58	.93	.84	.59
	3/16	3.71	1.09	.96	.44	.94	.82	.59
2½ x 2½	½	7.7	2.25	1.2	.72	.74	.81	.49
	3/8	5.9	1.73	.98	.57	.75	.76	.49
	5/16	5.0	1.47	.85	.48	.76	.74	.49
	¼	4.1	1.19	.70	.39	.77	.72	.49
	3/16	3.07	.90	.55	.30	.78	.69	.49
2 x 2	3/8	4.7	1.36	.48	.35	.59	.64	.39
	5/16	3.92	1.15	.42	.30	.60	.61	.39
	¼	3.19	.94	.35	.25	.61	.59	.39
	3/16	2.44	.71	.27	.19	.62	.57	.39
	1/8	1.65	.48	.19	.13	.63	.55	.40
1¾ x 1¾	¼	2.77	.81	.23	.19	.53	.53	.34
	3/16	2.12	.62	.18	.14	.54	.51	.34
	1/8	1.44	.42	.13	.10	.55	.48	.35
1½ x 1½	¼	2.34	.69	.14	.13	.45	.47	.29
	3/16	1.80	.53	.11	.10	.46	.44	.29
	1/8	1.23	.36	.08	.07	.47	.42	.30
1¼ x 1¼	¼	1.92	.56	.08	.09	.37	.40	.24
	3/16	1.48	.43	.06	.07	.38	.38	.24
	1/8	1.01	.30	.04	.05	.38	.36	.25
1 x 1	¼	1.49	.44	.04	.06	.29	.34	.20
	3/16	1.16	.34	.03	.04	.30	.32	.19
	1/8	.80	.23	.02	.03	.30	.30	.20

Table 7

ANGLES
UNEQUAL LEGS

PROPERTIES FOR DESIGNING

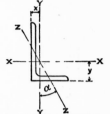

Size	Thick-ness	Weight per Foot	Area	AXIS X-X				AXIS Y-Y				AXIS Z-Z	
				I	S	r	y	I	S	r	x	r	Tan α
In.	In.	Lb.	In.²	In.⁴	In.³	In.	In.	In.⁴	In.³	In.	In.	In.	
9 x 4	1	40.8	12.00	97.0	17.6	2.84	3.50	12.0	4.0	1.00	1.00	.83	.203
	⅞	36.1	10.61	86.8	15.7	2.86	3.45	10.8	3.6	1.01	.95	.84	.208
	¾	31.3	9.19	76.1	13.6	2.88	3.41	9.6	3.1	1.02	.91	.84	.212
	⅝	26.3	7.73	64.9	11.5	2.90	3.36	8.3	2.6	1.04	.86	.85	.216
	⁹⁄₁₆	23.8	7.00	59.1	10.4	2.91	3.33	7.6	2.4	1.04	.83	.85	.218
	½	21.3	6.25	53.2	9.3	2.92	3.31	6.9	2.2	1.05	.81	.85	.220
8 x 6	1	44.2	13.00	80.8	15.1	2.49	2.65	38.8	8.9	1.73	1.65	1.28	.543
	⅞	39.1	11.48	72.3	13.4	2.51	2.61	34.9	7.9	1.74	1.61	1.28	.547
	¾	33.8	9.94	63.4	11.7	2.53	2.56	30.7	6.9	1.76	1.56	1.29	.551
	⅝	28.5	8.36	54.1	9.9	2.54	2.52	26.3	5.9	1.77	1.52	1.29	.554
	⁹⁄₁₆	25.7	7.56	49.3	9.0	2.55	2.50	24.0	5.3	1.78	1.50	1.30	.556
	½	23.0	6.75	44.3	8.0	2.56	2.47	21.7	4.8	1.79	1.47	1.30	.558
	⁷⁄₁₆	20.2	5.93	39.2	7.1	2.57	2.45	19.3	4.2	1.80	1.45	1.31	.560
8 x 4	1	37.4	11.00	69.6	14.1	2.52	3.05	11.6	3.9	1.03	1.05	.85	.247
	⅞	33.1	9.73	62.5	12.5	2.53	3.00	10.5	3.5	1.04	1.00	.85	.253
	¾	28.7	8.44	54.9	10.9	2.55	2.95	9.4	3.1	1.05	.95	.85	.258
	⅝	24.2	7.11	46.9	9.2	2.57	2.91	8.1	2.6	1.07	.91	.86	.262
	⁹⁄₁₆	21.9	6.43	42.8	8.4	2.58	2.88	7.4	2.4	1.07	.88	.86	.265
	½	19.6	5.75	38.5	7.5	2.59	2.86	6.7	2.2	1.08	.86	.86	.267
	⁷⁄₁₆	17.2	5.06	34.1	6.6	2.60	2.83	6.0	1.9	1.09	.83	.87	.269
7 x 4	⅞	30.2	8.86	42.9	9.7	2.20	2.55	10.2	3.5	1.07	1.05	.86	.318
	¾	26.2	7.69	37.8	8.4	2.22	2.51	9.1	3.0	1.09	1.01	.86	.324
	⅝	22.1	6.48	32.4	7.1	2.24	2.46	7.8	2.6	1.10	.96	.86	.329
	⁹⁄₁₆	20.0	5.87	29.6	6.5	2.24	2.44	7.2	2.4	1.11	.94	.87	.332
	½	17.9	5.25	26.7	5.8	2.25	2.42	6.5	2.1	1.11	.92	.87	.335
	⁷⁄₁₆	15.8	4.62	23.7	5.1	2.26	2.39	5.8	1.9	1.12	.89	.88	.337
	⅜	13.6	3.98	20.6	4.4	2.27	2.37	5.1	1.6	1.13	.87	.88	.339

Table 7 (*continued*)

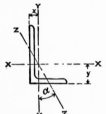

ANGLES
UNEQUAL LEGS

PROPERTIES FOR DESIGNING

Size	Thickness	Weight per Foot	Area	AXIS X-X				AXIS Y-Y				AXIS Z-Z	
				I	S	r	y	I	S	r	x	r	Tan α
In.	In.	Lb.	In.^{2}	In.^{4}	In.^{3}	In.	In.	In.^{4}	In.^{3}	In.	In.	In.	
6 x 4	⅞	27.2	7.98	27.7	7.2	1.86	2.12	9.8	3.4	1.11	1.12	.86	.421
	¾	23.6	6.94	24.5	6.3	1.88	2.08	8.7	3.0	1.12	1.08	.86	.428
	⅝	20.0	5.86	21.1	5.3	1.90	2.03	7.5	2.5	1.13	1.03	.86	.435
	⁹⁄₁₆	18.1	5.31	19.3	4.8	1.90	2.01	6.9	2.3	1.14	1.01	.87	.438
	½	16.2	4.75	17.4	4.3	1.91	1.99	6.3	2.1	1.15	.99	.87	.440
	⁷⁄₁₆	14.3	4.18	15.5	3.8	1.92	1.96	5.6	1.9	1.16	.96	.87	.443
	⅜	12.3	3.61	13.5	3.3	1.93	1.94	4.9	1.6	1.17	.94	.88	.446
	⁵⁄₁₆	10.3	3.03	11.4	2.8	1.94	1.92	4.2	1.4	1.17	.92	.88	.449
6 x 3½	½	15.3	4.50	16.6	4.2	1.92	2.08	4.3	1.6	.97	.83	.76	.344
	⅜	11.7	3.42	12.9	3.2	1.94	2.04	3.3	1.2	.99	.79	.77	.350
	⁵⁄₁₆	9.8	2.87	10.9	2.7	1.95	2.01	2.9	1.0	1.00	.76	.77	.352
	¼	7.9	2.31	8.9	2.2	1.96	1.99	2.3	0.85	1.01	.74	.78	.355
5 x 3½	¾	19.8	5.81	13.9	4.3	1.55	1.75	5.6	2.2	.98	1.00	.75	.464
	⅝	16.8	4.92	12.0	3.7	1.56	1.70	4.8	1.9	.99	.95	.75	.472
	½	13.6	4.00	10.0	3.0	1.58	1.66	4.1	1.6	1.01	.91	.75	.479
	⁷⁄₁₆	12.0	3.53	8.9	2.6	1.59	1.63	3.6	1.4	1.01	.88	.76	.482
	⅜	10.4	3.05	7.8	2.3	1.60	1.61	3.2	1.2	1.02	.86	.76	.486
	⁵⁄₁₆	8.7	2.56	6.6	1.9	1.61	1.59	2.7	1.0	1.03	.84	.76	.489
	¼	7.0	2.06	5.4	1.6	1.61	1.56	2.2	.83	1.04	.81	.76	.492
5 x 3	½	12.8	3.75	9.5	2.9	1.59	1.75	2.6	1.1	.83	.75	.65	.357
	⁷⁄₁₆	11.3	3.31	8.4	2.6	1.60	1.73	2.3	1.0	.84	.73	.65	.361
	⅜	9.8	2.86	7.4	2.2	1.61	1.70	2.0	.89	.84	.70	.65	.364
	⁵⁄₁₆	8.2	2.40	6.3	1.9	1.61	1.68	1.8	.75	.85	.68	.66	.368
	¼	6.6	1.94	5.1	1.5	1.62	1.66	1.4	.61	.86	.66	.66	.371

Table 7 (continued)

ANGLES
UNEQUAL LEGS

PROPERTIES FOR DESIGNING

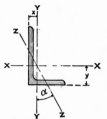

Size	Thick-ness	Weight per Foot	Area	AXIS X-X				AXIS Y-Y				AXIS Z-Z	
				I	S	r	y	I	S	r	x	r	Tan α
In.	In.	Lb.	In.²	In.⁴	In.³	In.	In.	In.⁴	In.³	In.	In.	In.	
4 x 3½	⅝	14.7	4.30	6.4	2.4	1.22	1.29	4.5	1.8	1.03	1.04	.72	.745
	½	11.9	3.50	5.3	1.9	1.23	1.25	3.8	1.5	1.04	1.00	.72	.750
	⁷⁄₁₆	10.6	3.09	4.8	1.7	1.24	1.23	3.4	1.4	1.05	.98	.72	.753
	⅜	9.1	2.67	4.2	1.5	1.25	1.21	3.0	1.2	1.06	.96	.73	.755
	⁵⁄₁₆	7.7	2.25	3.6	1.3	1.26	1.18	2.6	1.0	1.07	.93	.73	.757
	¼	6.2	1.81	2.9	1.0	1.27	1.16	2.1	.81	1.07	.91	.73	.759
4 x 3	⅝	13.6	3.98	6.0	2.3	1.23	1.37	2.9	1.4	.85	.87	.64	.534
	½	11.1	3.25	5.1	1.9	1.25	1.33	2.4	1.1	.86	.83	.64	.543
	⁷⁄₁₆	9.8	2.87	4.5	1.7	1.25	1.30	2.2	1.0	.87	.80	.64	.547
	⅜	8.5	2.48	4.0	1.5	1.26	1.28	1.9	.87	.88	.78	.64	.551
	⁵⁄₁₆	7.2	2.09	3.4	1.2	1.27	1.26	1.7	.73	.89	.76	.65	.554
	¼	5.8	1.69	2.8	1.0	1.28	1.24	1.4	.60	.90	.74	.65	.558
3½ x 3	½	10.2	3.00	3.5	1.5	1.07	1.13	2.3	1.1	.88	.88	.62	.714
	⁷⁄₁₆	9.1	2.65	3.1	1.3	1.08	1.10	2.1	.98	.89	.85	.62	.718
	⅜	7.9	2.30	2.7	1.1	1.09	1.08	1.9	.85	.90	.83	.62	.721
	⁵⁄₁₆	6.6	1.93	2.3	.95	1.10	1.06	1.6	.72	.90	.81	.63	.724
	¼	5.4	1.56	1.9	.78	1.11	1.04	1.3	.59	.91	.79	.63	.727
3½ x 2½	½	9.4	2.75	3.2	1.4	1.09	1.20	1.4	.76	.70	.70	.53	.486
	⁷⁄₁₆	8.3	2.43	2.9	1.3	1.09	1.18	1.2	.68	.71	.68	.54	.491
	⅜	7.2	2.11	2.6	1.1	1.10	1.16	1.1	.59	.72	.66	.54	.496
	⁵⁄₁₆	6.1	1.78	2.2	.93	1.11	1.14	.94	.50	.73	.64	.54	.501
	¼	4.9	1.44	1.8	.75	1.12	1.11	.78	.41	.74	.61	.54	.506

Table 7 (continued)

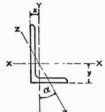

ANGLES
UNEQUAL LEGS

PROPERTIES FOR DESIGNING

Size	Thickness	Weight per Foot	Area	AXIS X-X				AXIS Y-Y				AXIS Z-Z	
				I	S	r	y	I	S	r	x	r	Tan α
In.	In.	Lb.	In.^{2}	In.^{4}	In.^{3}	In.	In.	In.^{4}	In.^{3}	In.	In.	In.	
3 x 2½	½	8.5	2.50	2.1	1.0	.91	1.00	1.3	.74	.72	.75	.52	.667
	7/16	7.6	2.21	1.9	.93	.92	.98	1.2	.66	.73	.73	.52	.672
	3/8	6.6	1.92	1.7	.81	.93	.96	1.0	.58	.74	.71	.52	.676
	5/16	5.6	1.62	1.4	.69	.94	.93	.90	.49	.74	.68	.53	.680
	¼	4.5	1.31	1.2	.56	.95	.91	.74	.40	.75	.66	.53	.684
3 x 2	½	7.7	2.25	1.9	1.0	.92	1.08	.67	.47	.55	.58	.43	.414
	7/16	6.8	2.00	1.7	.89	.93	1.06	.61	.42	.55	.56	.43	.421
	3/8	5.9	1.73	1.5	.78	.94	1.04	.54	.37	.56	.54	.43	.428
	5/16	5.0	1.47	1.3	.66	.95	1.02	.47	.32	.57	.52	.43	.435
	¼	4.1	1.19	1.1	.54	.95	.99	.39	.26	.57	.49	.43	.440
	3/16	3.07	.90	.84	.41	.97	.97	.31	.20	.58	.47	.44	.446
2½ x 2	3/8	5.3	1.55	.91	.55	.77	.83	.51	.36	.58	.58	.42	.614
	5/16	4.5	1.31	.79	.47	.78	.81	.45	.31	.58	.56	.42	.620
	¼	3.62	1.06	.65	.38	.78	.79	.37	.25	.59	.54	.42	.626
	3/16	2.75	.81	.51	.29	.79	.76	.29	.20	.60	.51	.43	.631
2½x1½	3/8	4.7	1.36	.82	.52	.78	.92	.22	.20	.40	.42	.32	.340
	5/16	3.92	1.15	.71	.44	.79	.90	.19	.17	.41	.40	.32	.349
	¼	3.19	.94	.59	.36	.79	.88	.16	.14	.41	.38	.32	.357
	3/16	2.44	.72	.46	.28	.80	.85	.13	.11	.42	.35	.33	.364
2 x 1½	¼	2.77	.81	.32	.24	.62	.66	.15	.14	.43	.41	.32	.543
	3/16	2.12	.62	.25	.18	.63	.64	.12	.11	.44	.39	.32	.551
	⅛	1.44	.42	.17	.13	.64	.62	.09	.08	.45	.37	.33	.558
1¾x1¼	¼	2.34	.69	.20	.18	.54	.60	.09	.10	.35	.35	.27	.486
	3/16	1.80	.53	.16	.14	.55	.58	.07	.08	.36	.33	.27	.496
	⅛	1.23	.36	.11	.09	.56	.56	.05	.05	.37	.31	.27	.506

Table 8

TWO UNEQUAL ANGLES

PROPERTIES OF SECTIONS

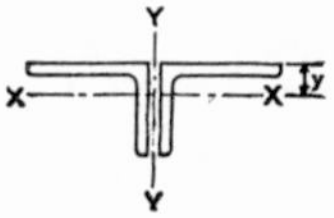

SHORT LEGS BACK TO BACK

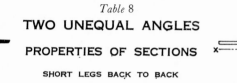

Size	Thickness	Weight per Ft. 2 Angles	Area of 2 Angles	AXIS X-X				RADII OF GYRATION ABOUT AXIS Y-Y					
				I	S	r	y	Back to Back of Angles, Inches					
								0	¼	⅜	½	⅝	¾
In.	In.	Lb.	In.²	In.⁴	In.³	In.	In.						
9 x 4	1	81.6	24.00	24.0	8.0	1.00	1.00	4.51	4.61	4.66	4.71	4.76	4.80
	⅞	72.2	21.22	21.6	7.2	1.01	.95	4.48	4.58	4.63	4.68	4.73	4.78
	¾	62.6	18.38	19.2	6.2	1.02	.91	4.46	4.56	4.61	4.65	4.70	4.75
	⅝	52.6	15.46	16.6	5.2	1.04	.86	4.43	4.53	4.58	4.63	4.68	4.73
	⁹⁄₁₆	47.6	14.00	15.2	4.8	1.04	.83	4.42	4.51	4.56	4.61	4.66	4.71
	½	42.6	12.50	13.8	4.4	1.05	.81	4.41	4.51	4.55	4.60	4.65	4.70
8 x 6	1	88.4	26.00	77.6	17.8	1.73	1.65	3.64	3.73	3.78	3.82	3.87	3.92
	⅞	78.2	22.96	69.7	15.9	1.74	1.61	3.62	3.71	3.76	3.81	3.85	3.90
	¾	67.6	19.88	61.4	13.8	1.76	1.56	3.60	3.69	3.73	3.78	3.83	3.87
	⅝	57.0	16.72	52.7	11.8	1.77	1.52	3.58	3.67	3.72	3.76	3.81	3.85
	⁹⁄₁₆	51.4	15.12	48.1	10.7	1.78	1.50	3.57	3.66	3.70	3.75	3.79	3.84
	½	46.0	13.50	43.4	9.6	1.79	1.47	3.56	3.65	3.69	3.74	3.78	3.83
	⁷⁄₁₆	40.4	11.86	38.5	8.5	1.80	1.45	3.55	3.64	3.68	3.73	3.77	3.82
8 x 4	1	74.8	22.00	23.3	7.9	1.03	1.05	3.95	4.05	4.10	4.15	4.20	4.25
	⅞	66.2	19.46	21.1	7.0	1.04	1.00	3.93	4.02	4.07	4.12	4.17	4.22
	¾	57.4	16.88	18.7	6.1	1.05	.95	3.90	3.99	4.04	4.09	4.14	4.19
	⅝	48.4	14.22	16.2	5.2	1.07	.91	3.88	3.98	4.02	4.07	4.12	4.17
	⁹⁄₁₆	43.8	12.86	14.8	4.8	1.07	.88	3.87	3.96	4.01	4.06	4.10	4.15
	½	39.2	11.50	13.5	4.3	1.08	.86	3.86	3.95	4.00	4.05	4.09	4.14
	⁷⁄₁₆	34.4	10.12	12.0	3.8	1.09	.83	3.85	3.94	3.99	4.04	4.07	4.12
7 x 4	⅞	60.4	17.72	20.4	6.9	1.07	1.05	3.37	3.46	3.51	3.56	3.61	3.66
	¾	52.4	15.38	18.1	6.1	1.09	1.01	3.35	3.44	3.49	3.54	3.59	3.64
	⅝	44.2	12.96	15.7	5.2	1.10	.96	3.32	3.42	3.47	3.51	3.56	3.61
	⁹⁄₁₆	40.0	11.74	14.4	4.8	1.11	.94	3.32	3.41	3.46	3.50	3.55	3.60
	½	35.8	10.50	13.0	4.2	1.11	.92	3.31	3.40	3.45	3.49	3.54	3.59
	⁷⁄₁₆	31.6	9.24	11.6	3.8	1.12	.89	3.29	3.39	3.43	3.48	3.53	3.57
	⅜	27.2	7.96	10.2	3.3	1.13	.87	3.28	3.38	3.42	3.47	3.52	3.56
6 x 4	⅞	54.4	15.96	19.5	6.8	1.11	1.12	2.82	2.92	2.97	3.02	3.06	3.11
	¾	47.2	13.88	17.4	5.9	1.12	1.08	2.80	2.90	2.95	2.99	3.04	3.09
	⅝	40.0	11.72	15.0	5.1	1.13	1.03	2.78	2.87	2.92	2.97	3.01	3.06
	⁹⁄₁₆	36.2	10.62	13.8	4.6	1.14	1.01	2.77	2.86	2.91	2.96	3.00	3.05
	½	32.4	9.50	12.5	4.2	1.15	.99	2.76	2.85	2.90	2.95	2.99	3.04
	⁷⁄₁₆	28.6	8.36	11.2	3.7	1.16	.96	2.75	2.84	2.88	2.93	2.98	3.03
	⅜	24.6	7.22	9.8	3.2	1.17	.94	2.74	2.83	2.87	2.92	2.97	3.02
6 x 3½	½	30.6	9.00	8.5	3.2	.97	.83	2.83	2.92	2.97	3.02	3.07	3.12
	⅜	23.4	6.84	6.7	2.5	.99	.79	2.81	2.90	2.95	3.00	3.05	3.09
	⁵⁄₁₆	19.6	5.74	5.7	2.1	1.00	.76	2.80	2.89	2.94	2.99	3.03	3.08
5 x 3½	¾	39.6	11.62	11.1	4.4	.98	1.00	2.34	2.43	2.48	2.53	2.58	2.63
	⅝	33.6	9.84	9.7	3.8	.99	.95	2.31	2.40	2.45	2.50	2.55	2.60
	½	27.2	8.00	8.1	3.1	1.01	.91	2.29	2.38	2.43	2.48	2.53	2.58
	⁷⁄₁₆	24.0	7.06	7.3	2.8	1.01	.88	2.28	2.37	2.41	2.46	2.51	2.56
	⅜	20.8	6.10	6.4	2.4	1.02	.86	2.27	2.36	2.40	2.45	2.50	2.55
	⁵⁄₁₆	17.4	5.12	5.4	2.0	1.03	.84	2.26	2.35	2.38	2.43	2.48	2.53
5 x 3	½	25.6	7.50	5.2	2.3	.83	.75	2.36	2.46	2.50	2.55	2.60	2.65
	⅜	19.6	5.72	4.1	1.8	.84	.70	2.34	2.43	2.48	2.53	2.58	2.63
	⁵⁄₁₆	16.4	4.80	3.5	1.5	.85	.68	2.33	2.42	2.47	2.52	2.57	2.62

Table 8 (*continued*)

TWO UNEQUAL ANGLES

PROPERTIES OF SECTIONS

SHORT LEGS BACK TO BACK

Size	Thick-ness	Weight per Ft. 2 Angles	Area of 2 Angles	AXIS X-X				RADII OF GYRATION ABOUT AXIS Y-Y					
								Back to Back of Angles, Inches					
				I	S	r	y	0	$\frac{1}{4}$	$\frac{3}{8}$	$\frac{1}{2}$	$\frac{5}{8}$	$\frac{3}{4}$
In.	In.	Lb.	In.^{2}	In.^{4}	In.^{3}	In.	In.						
4 x 3½	$\frac{5}{8}$	29.4	8.60	9.0	3.7	1.03	1.04	1.77	1.87	1.91	1.96	2.01	2.06
	$\frac{1}{2}$	23.8	7.00	7.6	3.0	1.04	1.00	1.76	1.85	1.89	1.94	1.99	2.04
	$\frac{7}{16}$	21.2	6.18	6.8	2.7	1.05	.98	1.75	1.84	1.89	1.94	1.98	2.03
	$\frac{3}{8}$	18.2	5.34	6.0	2.3	1.06	.96	1.74	1.83	1.88	1.92	1.97	2.02
	$\frac{5}{16}$	15.4	4.50	5.1	2.0	1.07	.93	1.73	1.81	1.86	1.91	1.96	2.00
	$\frac{1}{4}$	12.4	3.62	4.2	1.6	1.07	.91	1.72	1.80	1.85	1.90	1.94	1.99
4 x 3	$\frac{5}{8}$	27.2	7.96	5.7	2.7	.85	.87	1.84	1.94	1.99	2.03	2.08	2.14
	$\frac{1}{2}$	22.2	6.50	4.8	2.2	.86	.83	1.82	1.92	1.96	2.01	2.06	2.11
	$\frac{7}{16}$	19.6	5.74	4.4	2.0	.87	.80	1.81	1.90	1.95	1.99	2.04	2.09
	$\frac{3}{8}$	17.0	4.96	3.8	1.7	.88	.78	1.80	1.89	1.94	1.98	2.03	2.08
	$\frac{5}{16}$	14.4	4.18	3.3	1.5	.89	.76	1.79	1.88	1.93	1.97	2.02	2.07
	$\frac{1}{4}$	11.6	3.38	2.7	1.2	.90	.74	1.78	1.87	1.92	1.96	2.01	2.06
3½ x 3	$\frac{1}{2}$	20.4	6.00	4.7	2.2	.88	.88	1.56	1.65	1.70	1.75	1.80	1.85
	$\frac{7}{16}$	18.2	5.30	4.2	2.0	.89	.85	1.54	1.63	1.68	1.73	1.78	1.83
	$\frac{3}{8}$	15.8	4.60	3.7	1.7	.90	.83	1.53	1.62	1.67	1.72	1.77	1.82
	$\frac{5}{16}$	13.2	3.86	3.2	1.4	.90	.81	1.52	1.61	1.66	1.71	1.76	1.81
	$\frac{1}{4}$	10.8	3.12	2.6	1.2	.91	.79	1.52	1.61	1.65	1.70	1.75	1.80
3½x2½	$\frac{1}{2}$	18.8	5.50	2.7	1.5	.70	.70	1.62	1.71	1.76	1.81	1.86	1.91
	$\frac{7}{16}$	16.6	4.86	2.5	1.4	.71	.68	1.61	1.70	1.75	1.80	1.85	1.90
	$\frac{3}{8}$	14.4	4.22	2.2	1.2	.72	.66	1.61	1.69	1.74	1.79	1.84	1.89
	$\frac{5}{16}$	12.2	3.56	1.9	1.0	.73	.64	1.60	1.68	1.73	1.77	1.82	1.88
	$\frac{1}{4}$	9.8	2.88	1.6	0.8	.74	.61	1.58	1.67	1.71	1.76	1.81	1.86
3 x 2½	$\frac{1}{2}$	17.0	5.00	2.6	1.5	.72	.75	1.35	1.45	1.50	1.55	1.60	1.65
	$\frac{7}{16}$	15.2	4.42	2.4	1.3	.73	.73	1.34	1.44	1.49	1.54	1.59	1.64
	$\frac{3}{8}$	13.2	3.84	2.1	1.2	.74	.71	1.34	1.43	1.48	1.53	1.58	1.63
	$\frac{5}{16}$	11.2	3.24	1.8	1.0	.74	.68	1.32	1.41	1.46	1.51	1.56	1.60
	$\frac{1}{4}$	9.0	2.62	1.5	0.8	.75	.66	1.31	1.40	1.45	1.50	1.55	1.60
3 x 2	$\frac{1}{2}$	15.4	4.50	1.3	0.9	.55	.58	1.42	1.52	1.57	1.62	1.67	1.73
	$\frac{7}{16}$	13.6	4.00	1.2	0.8	.55	.56	1.41	1.51	1.56	1.61	1.65	1.71
	$\frac{3}{8}$	11.8	3.46	1.1	0.7	.56	.54	1.40	1.49	1.54	1.59	1.64	1.69
	$\frac{5}{16}$	10.0	2.94	0.9	0.6	.57	.52	1.39	1.48	1.53	1.58	1.63	1.68
	$\frac{1}{4}$	8.2	2.38	0.8	0.5	.57	.49	1.38	1.47	1.52	1.57	1.62	1.67
	$\frac{3}{16}$	6.1	1.80	0.6	0.4	.58	.47	1.37	1.46	1.51	1.56	1.61	1.66
2½ x 2	$\frac{3}{8}$	10.6	3.10	1.0	0.7	.58	.58	1.13	1.22	1.27	1.32	1.38	1.43
	$\frac{5}{16}$	9.0	2.62	0.9	0.6	.58	.56	1.12	1.21	1.26	1.31	1.37	1.42
	$\frac{1}{4}$	7.2	2.12	0.7	0.5	.59	.54	1.11	1.20	1.25	1.30	1.35	1.40
	$\frac{3}{16}$	5.5	1.62	0.6	0.4	.60	.51	1.10	1.19	1.24	1.29	1.34	1.38

Table 8 *(continued)*

TWO UNEQUAL ANGLES

PROPERTIES OF SECTIONS

LONG LEGS BACK TO BACK

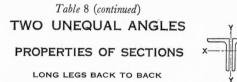

Size	Thick-ness	Weight per Ft. 2 Angles	Area of 2 Angles	AXIS X-X				RADII OF GYRATION ABOUT AXIS Y-Y Back to Back of Angles, Inches					
				I	S	r	y	0	1/4	3/8	1/2	5/8	3/4
In.	In.	Lb.	In.²	In.⁴	In.³	In.	In.						
9 x 4	1	81.6	24.00	194.0	35.2	2.84	3.50	1.41	1.50	1.55	1.60	1.65	1.70
	7/8	72.2	21.22	173.6	31.4	2.86	3.45	1.39	1.47	1.52	1.57	1.62	1.67
	3/4	62.6	18.38	152.2	27.2	2.88	3.41	1.37	1.45	1.50	1.55	1.59	1.64
	5/8	52.6	15.46	129.8	23.0	2.90	3.36	1.35	1.43	1.47	1.52	1.56	1.61
	9/16	47.6	14.00	118.2	20.8	2.91	3.33	1.33	1.41	1.46	1.50	1.55	1.59
	1/2	42.6	12.50	106.4	18.6	2.92	3.31	1.33	1.41	1.45	1.49	1.54	1.58
8 x 6	1	88.4	26.00	161.6	30.2	2.49	2.65	2.39	2.48	2.52	2.57	2.61	2.66
	7/8	78.2	22.96	144.6	26.8	2.51	2.61	2.37	2.46	2.50	2.55	2.59	2.64
	3/4	67.6	19.88	126.8	23.3	2.53	2.56	2.35	2.44	2.48	2.52	2.57	2.61
	5/8	57.0	16.72	108.2	19.7	2.54	2.52	2.34	2.42	2.46	2.51	2.55	2.60
	9/16	51.4	15.12	98.5	17.9	2.55	2.50	2.33	2.41	2.46	2.50	2.54	2.59
	1/2	46.0	13.50	88.6	16.0	2.56	2.47	2.32	2.40	2.44	2.48	2.53	2.57
	7/16	40.4	11.86	78.4	14.1	2.57	2.45	2.31	2.39	2.43	2.47	2.52	2.56
8 x 4	1	74.8	22.00	139.3	28.1	2.52	3.05	1.47	1.56	1.61	1.66	1.71	1.76
	7/8	66.2	19.46	124.9	25.0	2.53	3.00	1.44	1.53	1.58	1.63	1.68	1.72
	3/4	57.4	16.88	109.8	21.8	2.55	2.95	1.42	1.50	1.55	1.60	1.64	1.69
	5/8	48.4	14.22	93.8	18.4	2.57	2.91	1.40	1.49	1.53	1.58	1.62	1.67
	9/16	43.8	12.86	85.6	16.8	2.58	2.88	1.39	1.47	1.51	1.56	1.60	1.65
	1/2	39.2	11.50	77.0	15.0	2.59	2.86	1.38	1.46	1.51	1.55	1.60	1.64
	7/16	34.4	10.12	68.2	13.2	2.60	2.83	1.37	1.45	1.49	1.53	1.58	1.62
7 x 4	7/8	60.4	17.72	85.8	19.3	2.20	2.55	1.50	1.59	1.64	1.68	1.73	1.78
	3/4	52.4	15.38	75.6	16.8	2.22	2.51	1.48	1.57	1.62	1.66	1.71	1.76
	5/8	44.2	12.96	64.8	14.3	2.24	2.46	1.46	1.55	1.59	1.64	1.68	1.73
	9/16	40.0	11.74	59.2	13.0	2.24	2.44	1.45	1.54	1.58	1.62	1.67	1.72
	1/2	35.8	10.50	53.3	11.6	2.25	2.42	1.45	1.53	1.57	1.62	1.66	1.71
	7/16	31.6	9.24	47.4	10.2	2.26	2.39	1.43	1.51	1.55	1.60	1.65	1.69
	3/8	27.2	7.96	41.1	8.9	2.27	2.37	1.43	1.51	1.55	1.59	1.64	1.68
6 x 4	7/8	54.4	15.96	55.5	14.3	1.86	2.12	1.57	1.66	1.71	1.76	1.81	1.86
	3/4	47.2	13.88	49.0	12.5	1.88	2.08	1.55	1.64	1.69	1.74	1.79	1.84
	5/8	40.0	11.72	42.1	10.6	1.90	2.03	1.53	1.62	1.66	1.71	1.76	1.80
	9/16	36.2	10.62	38.5	9.7	1.90	2.01	1.52	1.61	1.66	1.70	1.75	1.79
	1/2	32.4	9.50	34.8	8.7	1.91	1.99	1.52	1.60	1.65	1.69	1.74	1.78
	7/16	28.6	8.36	31.0	7.7	1.92	1.96	1.50	1.59	1.63	1.68	1.72	1.77
	3/8	24.6	7.22	26.9	6.6	1.93	1.94	1.50	1.58	1.62	1.67	1.71	1.76
6 x 3½	1/2	30.6	9.00	33.2	8.5	1.92	2.08	1.27	1.36	1.40	1.45	1.49	1.55
	3/8	23.4	6.84	25.7	6.5	1.94	2.04	1.26	1.34	1.39	1.43	1.48	1.53
	5/16	19.6	5.74	21.8	5.5	1.95	2.01	1.26	1.33	1.38	1.42	1.46	1.51
5 x 3½	3/4	39.6	11.62	27.8	8.6	1.55	1.75	1.40	1.49	1.54	1.59	1.64	1.69
	5/8	33.6	9.84	24.1	7.3	1.56	1.70	1.37	1.46	1.51	1.56	1.60	1.65
	1/2	27.2	8.00	20.0	6.0	1.58	1.66	1.36	1.44	1.49	1.54	1.58	1.63
	7/16	24.0	7.06	17.8	5.3	1.59	1.63	1.35	1.43	1.47	1.52	1.57	1.62
	3/8	20.8	6.10	15.6	4.6	1.60	1.61	1.34	1.42	1.46	1.51	1.55	1.60
	5/16	17.4	5.12	13.2	3.9	1.61	1.59	1.33	1.41	1.45	1.50	1.54	1.59
5 x 3	1/2	25.6	7.50	18.9	5.8	1.59	1.75	1.11	1.21	1.25	1.30	1.35	1.40
	3/8	19.6	5.72	14.7	4.5	1.61	1.70	1.09	1.18	1.23	1.27	1.32	1.37
	5/16	16.4	4.80	12.5	3.8	1.61	1.68	1.09	1.17	1.22	1.26	1.31	1.36

Table 8 (*continued*)

TWO UNEQUAL ANGLES

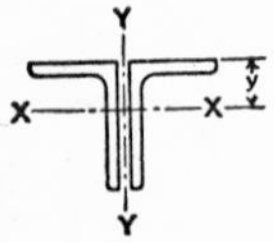

PROPERTIES OF SECTIONS

LONG LEGS BACK TO BACK

Size	Thickness	Weight per Ft. 2 Angles	Area of 2 Angles	AXIS X-X				RADII OF GYRATION ABOUT AXIS Y-Y					
								Back to Back of Angles, Inches					
				I	S	r	y	0	¼	⅜	½	⅝	¾
In.	In.	Lb.	In.²	In.⁴	In.³	In.	In.						
4 x 3½	⅝	29.4	8.60	12.7	4.7	1.22	1.29	1.46	1.55	1.60	1.65	1.70	1.75
	½	23.8	7.00	10.6	3.9	1.23	1.25	1.44	1.53	1.58	1.63	1.67	1.72
	⁷⁄₁₆	21.2	6.18	9.5	3.4	1.24	1.23	1.44	1.52	1.57	1.62	1.66	1.71
	⅜	18.2	5.34	8.4	3.0	1.25	1.21	1.43	1.52	1.56	1.61	1.66	1.70
	⁵⁄₁₆	15.4	4.50	7.1	2.5	1.26	1.18	1.42	1.50	1.55	1.59	1.64	1.69
	¼	12.4	3.62	5.8	2.1	1.27	1.16	1.41	1.49	1.54	1.58	1.63	1.67
4 x 3	⅝	27.2	7.96	12.1	4.6	1.23	1.37	1.22	1.31	1.36	1.41	1.46	1.51
	½	22.2	6.50	10.1	3.8	1.25	1.33	1.20	1.29	1.33	1.38	1.43	1.48
	⁷⁄₁₆	19.6	5.74	9.0	3.4	1.25	1.30	1.18	1.27	1.32	1.36	1.41	1.46
	⅜	17.0	4.96	7.9	2.9	1.26	1.28	1.18	1.26	1.31	1.35	1.40	1.45
	⁵⁄₁₆	14.4	4.18	6.8	2.5	1.27	1.26	1.17	1.25	1.30	1.35	1.39	1.44
	¼	11.6	3.38	5.5	2.0	1.28	1.24	1.16	1.25	1.29	1.34	1.38	1.43
3½ x 3	½	20.4	6.00	6.9	2.9	1.07	1.13	1.25	1.34	1.38	1.43	1.48	1.53
	⁷⁄₁₆	18.2	5.30	6.2	2.6	1.08	1.10	1.23	1.32	1.37	1.41	1.46	1.51
	⅜	15.8	4.60	5.4	2.3	1.09	1.08	1.22	1.31	1.36	1.40	1.45	1.50
	⁵⁄₁₆	13.2	3.86	4.7	1.9	1.10	1.06	1.22	1.30	1.35	1.39	1.44	1.49
	¼	10.8	3.12	3.8	1.6	1.11	1.04	1.21	1.29	1.34	1.38	1.43	1.48
3½x2½	½	18.8	5.50	6.5	2.8	1.09	1.20	.99	1.08	1.13	1.18	1.23	1.29
	⁷⁄₁₆	16.6	4.86	5.8	2.5	1.09	1.18	.98	1.07	1.12	1.17	1.22	1.27
	⅜	14.4	4.22	5.1	2.2	1.10	1.16	.97	1.07	1.11	1.16	1.21	1.26
	⁵⁄₁₆	12.2	3.56	4.4	1.9	1.11	1.14	.96	1.05	1.10	1.15	1.20	1.24
	¼	9.8	2.88	3.6	1.5	1.12	1.11	.95	1.04	1.09	1.13	1.18	1.23
3 x 2½	½	17.0	5.00	4.2	2.1	.91	1.00	1.04	1.14	1.18	1.23	1.28	1.34
	⁷⁄₁₆	15.2	4.42	3.8	1.9	.92	.98	1.03	1.12	1.17	1.22	1.27	1.33
	⅜	13.2	3.84	3.3	1.6	.93	.96	1.02	1.11	1.16	1.21	1.26	1.31
	⁵⁄₁₆	11.2	3.24	2.8	1.4	.94	.93	1.01	1.10	1.14	1.19	1.24	1.29
	¼	9.0	2.62	2.3	1.1	.95	.91	1.00	1.09	1.13	1.18	1.23	1.28
3 x 2	½	15.4	4.50	3.8	2.0	.92	1.08	.80	.89	.94	1.00	1.04	1.10
	⁷⁄₁₆	13.6	4.00	3.5	1.8	.93	1.06	.79	.88	.93	.98	1.03	1.09
	⅜	11.8	3.46	3.1	1.6	.94	1.04	.78	.87	.92	.97	1.02	1.07
	⁵⁄₁₆	10.0	2.94	2.6	1.3	.95	1.02	.77	.86	.90	.95	1.00	1.06
	¼	8.2	2.38	2.2	1.1	.96	.99	.75	.84	.89	.93	.99	1.04
	³⁄₁₆	6.14	1.80	1.7	0.8	.97	.97	.75	.83	.88	.93	.98	1.03
2½ x 2	⅜	10.6	3.10	1.8	1.1	.77	.83	.82	.91	.96	1.01	1.06	1.11
	⁵⁄₁₆	9.0	2.62	1.6	0.9	.78	.81	.81	.91	.95	1.00	1.05	1.10
	¼	7.2	2.12	1.3	0.8	.78	.79	.80	.89	.94	.99	1.04	1.09
	³⁄₁₆	5.5	1.62	1.0	0.6	.79	.76	.79	.88	.92	.96	1.02	1.07

Table 9. *Section Moduli for Shapes Used as Beams*

Section Modulus	Shape	Section Modulus	Shape	Section Modulus	Shape
1105.1	36 WF 300	220.9	**24 WF 94**	98.2	**18 WF 55**
1031.2	36 WF 280	220.1	18 WF 114	97.5	12 WF 72
951.1	36 WF 260	216.0	14 WF 136	94.1	16 WF 58
892.5	36 WF 245	202.2	18 WF 105	92.2	14 WF 61
		202.0	14 WF 127		
835.5	**36 WF 230**	197.6	21 WF 96	89.0	**18 WF 50**
811.1	33 WF 240	197.6	24 I 100	88.4	18 I 54.7
				88.0	12 WF 65
740.6	**33 WF 220**	196.3	**24 WF 84**	86.1	10 WF 77
		189.4	14 WF 119		
669.6	**33 WF 200**	185.8	24 I 90	80.7	**16 WF 50**
		184.4	18 WF 96	80.1	10 WF 72
663.6	**36 WF 194**	182.5	12 WF 133	78.1	12 WF 58
649.9	30 WF 210	176.3	14 WF 111	77.8	14 WF 53
				74.5	18 ⊔ 58
621.2	**36 WF 182**	175.4	**24 WF 76**	73.7	10 WF 66
586.1	30 WF 190	173.9	24 I 79.9		
		168.0	21 WF 82	72.4	**16 WF 45**
579.1	**36 WF 170**	166.1	16 WF 96	70.7	12 WF 53
		163.6	14 WF 103	70.2	14 WF 48
541.0	**36 WF 160**	163.4	12 WF 120	69.1	18 ⊔ 51.9
528.2	30 WF 172	160.0	20 I 95	67.1	10 WF 60
		156.1	18 WF 85	64.7	12 WF 50
502.9	**36 WF 150**	151.3	16 WF 88		
492.8	27 WF 177			64.4	**16 WF 40**
486.4	33 WF 152	150.7	**21 WF 73**	64.2	15 I 50
		150.6	14 WF 95	63.7	18 ⊔ 45.8
446.8	**33 WF 141**	150.2	20 I 85	62.7	14 WF 43
444.5	27 WF 160	144.5	12 WF 106	61.0	18 ⊔ 42.7
413.5	24 WF 160	141.7	18 WF 77	60.4	10 WF 54
				60.4	8 WF 67
404.8	**33 WF 130**	139.9	**21 WF 68**	58.9	15 I 42.9
402.9	27 WF 145	138.1	14 WF 87	58.2	12 WF 45
379.7	30 WF 132	134.7	12 WF 99		
372.5	24 WF 145	130.9	14 WF 84	56.3	**16 WF 36**
		128.2	18 WF 70	54.6	14 WF 38
354.6	**30 WF 124**	127.8	16 WF 78	54.6	10 WF 49
330.7	24 WF 130			53.6	15 ⊔ 50
		126.4	**21 WF 62**	52.0	8 WF 58
327.9	**30 WF 116**	126.3	20 I 75	51.9	12 WF 40
317.2	21 WF 142	126.3	10 WF 112	50.3	12 I 50
		125.0	12 WF 92	49.1	10 WF 45
299.2	**30 WF 108**	121.1	14 WF 78		
299.2	27 WF 114	117.0	18 WF 64	48.5	**14 WF 34**
299.1	24 WF 120	116.9	20 I 65.4	46.2	15 ⊔ 40
284.1	21 WF 127	115.9	16 WF 71	45.9	12 WF 36
274.4	24 WF 110	115.7	12 WF 85	44.8	12 I 40.8
		112.4	10 WF 100	43.2	8 WF 48
266.3	**27 WF 102**	112.3	14 WF 74	42.2	10 WF 39
263.2	12 WF 190				
250.9	24 I 120	107.8	**18 WF 60**	41.8	**14 WF 30**
249.6	21 WF 112	107.1	12 WF 79	41.7	15 ⊔ 33.9
		104.2	16 WF 64	39.4	12 WF 31
248.9	**24 WF 100**	103.0	14 WF 68	37.8	12 I 35
		101.9	18 I 70	36.0	12 I 31.8
242.8	**27 WF 94**	99.7	10 WF 89	35.5	8 WF 40
234.3	24 I 105.9			35.0	10 WF 33
222.2	12 WF 161				

Table 9. Section Moduli for Shapes Used as Beams (continued)

Section Modulus	Shape	Source	Section Modulus	Shape	Source	Section Modulus	Shape	Source
34.1	12 WF 27	9	14.8	12 B 14	8	7.8	10 Jr 9	7
31.1	8 WF 35	2	14.2	8 I 18.4	1	7.8	8 B 10	2
30.8	10 WF 29	9	14.1	8 WF 17	9	7.7	7 ⊔ 14.75	1
29.2	10 I 35	1	14.0	8 M 17	6	7.3	6 I 12.5	1
28.9	8 M 34.3	3	13.8	10 B 15	9	7.2	6 B 12	2
27.4	8 WF 31	2	13.5	9 ⊔ 20	1	6.9	7 ⊔ 12.25	1
26.9	12 ⊔ 30	1	13.4	10 ⊔ 15.3	1			
			13.4	6 WF 20	2	6.5	10 Jr⊔ 8.4	7
26.4	10 WF 25	9	12.9	6 M 20	3	6.0	7 ⊔ 9.8	1
						6.0	5 I 14.75	1
25.3	12 B 22	9	12.0	12 Jr 11.8	7	5.8	6 ⊔ 13	1
24.4	10 I 25.4	1	12.0	7 I 20	1	5.4	4 WF 13	5
24.3	8 WF 28	2	11.8	8 B 15	2	5.2	4 M 13	4
23.9	12 ⊔ 25	1	11.3	9 ⊔ 15	1	5.1	6 B 8.5	2
			10.9	8 ⊔ 18.75	1	5.0	6 ⊔ 10.5	1
21.5	10 WF 21	9				4.8	5 I 10	1
			10.5	10 B 11.5	8			
21.4	12 B 19	9	10.5	9 ⊔ 13.4	1	4.7	8 Jr 6.5	7
21.4	12 ⊔ 20.7	1	10.4	7 I 15.3	1	4.4	10 Jr ⊔ 6.5	7
21.0	8 M 24	6	10.1	6 WF 15.5	2	4.3	6 ⊔ 8.2	1
			10.1	6 B 16	2			
21.0	14 B 17.2	7	9.9	8 B 13	2			
20.8	8 WF 24	2	9.9	5 WF 18.5	2	3.5	7 Jr 5.5	7
20.6	10 ⊔ 30	1	9.5	5 M 18.9	2	3.5	5 ⊔ 9	1
18.8	10 B 19	9				3.3	4 I 9.5	1
18.1	10 ⊔ 25	1	9.3	12 Jr ⊔ 10.6	7	3.0	5 ⊔ 6.7	1
			9.0	8 ⊔ 13.75	1	3.0	4 I 7.7	1
17.5	12 B 16.5	9	8.7	6 I 17.25	1			
17.0	8 WF 20	9	8.5	5 WF 16	2	2.4	6 Jr 4.4	7
16.8	6 WF 25	2	8.1	8 ⊔ 11.5	1	2.3	4 ⊔ 7.25	1
16.2	10 B 17	9				1.9	4 ⊔ 5.4	1
16.0	8 I 23	1				1.9	3 I 7.5	1
15.7	10 ⊔ 20	1				1.7	3 I 5.7	1
15.7	6 M 25	3				1.4	3 ⊔ 6	1
15.2	8 M 20	6						
						1.2	3 ⊔ 5	1
						1.1	3 ⊔ 4.1	1

Index to Source Numbers
1. All Structural Mills.
2. U. S. Steel, Bethlehem.
3. U. S. Steel, Inland.
4. U. S. Steel.
5. Bethlehem.
6. Phoenix.
7. Jones & Laughlin.
8. U. S. Steel, Bethlehem, Jones & Laughlin, Inland.
9. U. S. Steel, Bethlehem, Inland.

NOTE: On this page, if the bold-face shape at the head of the group is one which because of its "source" is not available for the particular job, examine the adjacent upper groups for a lighter shape that is available.

Table 10. *Allowable Stresses per Square Inch for Compression Members*

Main and Secondary Members, l/r not over 120, $f = 17000 - 0.485 \left(\dfrac{l}{r}\right)^2$						Secondary Members, l/r 121 to 200, $f = \dfrac{18000}{1 + \dfrac{l^2}{18000 r^2}}$				Main Members, l/r 121 to 200, $Do \times \left(1.6 - \dfrac{l/r}{200}\right)$			
$\dfrac{l}{r}$	Unit Stress ksi.	$\dfrac{l}{r}$	Unit Stress ksi.	$\dfrac{l}{r}$	Unit Stress ksi.	$\dfrac{l}{r}$	Unit Stress ksi.	$\dfrac{l}{r}$	Unit Stress ksi.	$\dfrac{l}{r}$	Unit Stress ksi.	$\dfrac{l}{r}$	Unit Stress ksi.
1	17.00	41	16.19	81	13.82	121	9.93	161	7.38	121	9.88	161	5.87
2	17.00	42	16.14	82	13.74	122	9.85	162	7.32	122	9.75	162	5.78
3	17.00	43	16.10	83	13.66	123	9.78	163	7.27	123	9.63	163	5.71
4	16.99	44	16.06	84	13.58	124	9.71	164	7.22	124	9.52	164	5.63
5	16.99	45	16.02	85	13.50	125	9.64	165	7.16	125	9.40	165	5.53
6	16.98	46	15.97	86	13.41	126	9.56	166	7.11	126	9.27	166	5.47
7	16.98	47	15.93	87	13.33	127	9.49	167	7.06	127	9.16	167	5.40
8	16.97	48	15.88	88	13.24	128	9.42	168	7.01	128	9.04	168	5.33
9	16.96	49	15.84	89	13.16	129	9.35	169	6.96	129	8.93	169	5.25
10	16.95	50	15.79	90	13.07	130	9.28	170	6.91	130	8.82	170	5.18
11	16.94	51	15.74	91	12.98	131	9.22	171	6.86	131	8.71	171	5.11
12	16.93	52	15.69	92	12.90	132	9.15	172	6.81	132	8.60	172	5.04
13	16.92	53	15.64	93	12.81	133	9.08	173	6.76	133	8.49	173	4.97
14	16.91	54	15.59	94	12.72	134	9.01	174	6.71	134	8.38	174	4.90
15	16.89	55	15.53	95	12.62	135	8.94	175	6.66	135	8.27	175	4.83
16	16.88	56	15.48	96	12.53	136	8.88	176	6.62	136	8.17	176	4.77
17	16.86	57	15.42	97	12.44	137	8.81	177	6.57	137	8.06	177	4.70
18	16.84	58	15.37	98	12.34	138	8.75	178	6.52	138	7.96	178	4.63
19	16.83	59	15.31	99	12.25	139	8.68	179	6.48	139	7.86	179	4.57
20	16.81	60	15.25	100	12.15	140	8.62	180	6.43	140	7.76	180	4.50
21	16.79	61	15.20	101	12.05	141	8.55	181	6.38	141	7.65	181	4.43
22	16.77	62	15.14	102	11.95	142	8.49	182	6.34	142	7.56	182	4.37
23	16.74	63	15.08	103	11.86	143	8.43	183	6.29	143	7.46	183	4.31
24	16.72	64	15.01	104	11.75	144	8.36	184	6.25	144	7.36	184	4.25
25	16.70	65	14.95	105	11.65	145	8.30	185	6.20	145	7.26	185	4.19
26	16.67	66	14.89	106	11.55	146	8.24	186	6.16	146	7.17	186	4.13
27	16.65	67	14.82	107	11.45	147	8.18	187	6.12	147	7.08	187	4.07
28	16.62	68	14.76	108	11.34	148	8.12	188	6.07	148	6.98	188	4.01
29	16.59	69	14.69	109	11.24	149	8.06	189	6.03	149	6.89	189	3.95
30	16.56	70	14.62	110	11.13	150	8.00	190	5.99	150	6.80	190	3.89
31	16.53	71	14.56	111	11.02	151	7.94	191	5.95	151	6.71	191	3.84
32	16.50	72	14.49	112	10.92	152	7.88	192	5.91	152	6.62	192	3.78
33	16.47	73	14.42	113	10.81	153	7.82	193	5.86	153	6.53	193	3.72
34	16.44	74	14.34	114	10.70	154	7.77	194	5.82	154	6.45	194	3.67
35	16.41	75	14.27	115	10.59	155	7.71	195	5.78	155	6.36	195	3.61
36	16.37	76	14.20	116	10.47	156	7.65	196	5.74	156	6.27	196	3.56
37	16.34	77	14.12	117	10.36	157	7.60	197	5.70	157	6.19	197	3.51
38	16.30	78	14.05	118	10.25	158	7.54	198	5.66	158	6.11	198	3.45
39	16.26	79	13.97	119	10.13	159	7.49	199	5.62	159	6.03	199	3.40
40	16.22	80	13.90	120	10.02	160	7.43	200	5.59	160	5.94	200	3.35

INDEX

ANSWERS TO PROBLEMS

Chapter 1

1-1. 31,800 psi

1-3. 6,000 lb

1-5. 14¼ in.

1-7. 1,600 psi

1-9. 1,440 psi

1-11. $s = 32,000$ psi
$s_n = s_s = 16,000$ psi

1-13. $s_n = 24,000$ psi
$s_s = 13,800$ psi

1-15. 9,000 lb

1-17. 36,000 lb with grain
10,800 lb across grain

1-19. 284,000 lb tension
170,000 lb shear

1-21. 4¾ in.

1-23. 3⁹⁄₁₆ in.

1-25. 3⅛ in.

1-27. 41,600 lb

1-29. 480 lb

1-31. 1¼ ft

1-33. 1⅛ in.

1-35. $\epsilon = 0.0002$ in. per in.

1-37. 95,500 psi

1-39. 55,200 lb tension
248,000 lb compression

1-41. 64,000 lb

1-43. 26,600 lb steady stress

1-45. 6⅜ in.

1-47. 3¹⁵⁄₁₆ in.

1-49. 3¹⁄₁₆ in.

1-51. 20.8 per cent elongation; 28.8 per cent reduction of area

1-53. 40.2 per cent elongation
33.2 per cent reduction of area

1-55. 35,200 psi elastic limit
50,000 psi ultimate strength

1-57. 82,400 lb

1-59. 338,000 lb

1-61. 0.326 in.

1-63. 1,199.358 in. at − 20°F

1-65. 0.235 in.

1-67. 71⁵⁷⁄₆₄ in.

1-69. 0.02 in.

1-71. 9,000 lb

1-73. 132,000 lb

Chapter 2

2-1. 39,600 lb

2-3. Fails in tension in plate

2-5. Yes

2-7. 63 per cent

2-9. 27 per cent

2-11. $t = \frac{5}{16}$ in.

$n = 7$ rivets

$P = 2\frac{1}{4}$ in.

2-13. $t = \frac{1}{4}$ in.

$n = 16$ rivets

$P = 2\frac{1}{4}$ in.

2-15. $t = \frac{5}{16}$ in.

$n = 7$ rivets

$P = 2\frac{11}{16}$ in.

2-17. 16 in.

2-19. 48,000 lb

2-21. 26 per cent greater load in welded construction

2-23. $\frac{3}{8}$-in. base *108,000*

2-25. 135,000 lb

2-27. 14 per cent stronger in welded construction

Chapter 3

3-1. $R_1 = 3,770$ lb

$R_2 = 2,910$ lb

3-3. $R_1 = 1,500$ lb

$R_2 = 1,800$ lb

3-5. $R_1 = 1,770$ lb

$R_2 = 4,330$ lb

3-7. $R_1 = 3,900$ lb

$R_2 = 1,520$ lb

3-9. $R_1 = 2,660$ lb

$R_2 = 2,740$ lb

3-11. $R_1 = R_2 = 2,350$ lb

3-13. $M_{R_2} = -6,880$ lb-ft

3-15. $M_{14} = 5,400$ lb-ft

3-17. $M_{10.3} = 7,900$ lb-ft

3-19. $M_{11} = 3,000$ lb-ft

3-21. $M = -52,800$ lb-ft

3-23. $M = -60,000$ lb-ft

3-25. $x = 12.7$ ft from left end

3-27. $x_1 = 7.8$ ft from left end

3-29. None

3-31. $x_1 = 5.5$ ft from left end

3-45. $M_{\max} = 148,000$ lb-ft

3-47. $M_{\max} = 169,000$ lb-ft

3-49. $M_{\max} = 38,400$ lb-ft

Chapter 4

4-1. $\bar{y} = 7.7$ in.

4-3. $\bar{y} = 7$ in.

4-5. $\bar{x} = 3.4$ in.

$\bar{y} = 2.5$ in.

4-6. $\bar{y} = 6.6$ in.

4-8. $\bar{y} = 6.7$ in.

4-10. $\bar{y} = 8.5$ in.

4-11. $I_x = 27$ in.^{4}

$I_y = 15$ in.^{4}

4-13. 850 in.^{4}

4-15. 358 in.^{4}

4-17. 3,860 in.^{4}

4-19. 2,014 in.^{4}

4-21. 1,790 in.^{4}

Chapter 5

5-1. 2,250 psi

5-3. 15,700 psi

5-5. $2\frac{1}{2}$ in. square

5-7. 5 WF 16

5-9. 10 Jr. 8.4

5-11. 4 WF 10

5-13. 6 by 8 in.

5-15. 2 by 4 in.

5-17. 14 WF 30

5-19. 4.2 ft

5-21. 14 WF 30

5-23. 18 WF 55

5-25. 6 by 10 in.

5-27. 10 by 10 in.

5-29. 15 in.

5-31. 4 by 8 in.
5-33. Two 5- by 5- by ½-in. angles

5-35. 62,500 lb.
5-37. 62,500 psi

Chapter 6

6-1. 60 in.
6-3. 500 ft
6-5. 0.281 in.
6-7. 0.157 in.
6-8. 0.502 in.
6-10. 0.16 in.

6-12. 0.76 in.
6-14. 1.01 in.
6-17. 12 by 12 in.
6-19. 0.32 in.
6-21. 0.60 in.

Chapter 7

7-1. 10 WF 25; $\Delta = 0.322$ in.
7-3. 8 I 23; $\Delta = 0.49$ in.
7-5. 16 WF 45; $\Delta = 0.236$ in.

7-7. 12 I 31.8; $\Delta = 0.226$ in.
7-9. $M_{\max} = 7,650$ lb-ft
7-11. $M_{\max} = 14,100$ lb-ft

Chapter 8

8-1. $s_w = 430$ psi
     $s_s = 9,120$ psi
8-3. 1¼ in.
8-5. $s_w = 800$ psi
     $s_s = 16,700$ psi
8-7. 720 lb per ft

8-9. 1,800 lb per ft
8-11. 1.63 sq in.
8-13. Five ⅝-in. rods
8-15. Five ⅝-in. rods.
8-17. 15 by 15 in.

Chapter 9

9-1. 540,000 lb
9-3. $P_{12} = 190,000$ lb
     $P_{24} = 75,000$ lb (main column)
9-5. 11.5 ft
9-7. 38.5 ft
9-9. 4 by 8 in.

9-11. 12 WF 40
9-13. 12 I 40.8
9-15. 93,000 lb
9-17. 660,000 lb
9-19. 3½ by 3½ in. square
9-21. $P_{25} = 34,000$ lb

Chapter 10

10-1. 125,500 lb-in.
10-3. 2,460 psi
10-5. 265,000 lb-in.
10-7. 577,000 lb-in.
10-9. 3,600 psi
10-11. $s_s = 15,300$ psi
10-13. 3.8°
10-15. 4 ft 4¼ in.
10-17. 101 hp

10-19. 845 hp
10-21. 50 rpm
10-23. 4½ in. diam
10-25. 6½ in. diam
10-27. $s = 5,540$ psi
       $s_s = 1,630$ psi
10-29. $e = \dfrac{4\pi R^2 n s_s}{E_s d}$
10-31. 8,800 psi